Target 9
Get back on track

Pearson Edexcel GCSE (9–1)
History

Early Elizabethan England, 1558–88

Georgina Blair

Pearson

Published by Pearson Education Limited, 80 Strand, London, WC2R 0RL.

www.pearsonschoolsandfecolleges.co.uk

Copies of official specifications for all Pearson qualifications may be found on the website: qualifications.pearson.com

Text and illustrations © Pearson Education Ltd 2018
Typeset and illustrated by Newgen KnowledgeWorks Pvt. Ltd. Chennai, India
Produced by Out of House Publishing Solutions

The right of Georgina Blair to be identified as author of this work has been asserted by her in accordance with the Copyright, Designs and Patents Act 1988.

First published 2018

21 20 19 18
10 9 8 7 6 5 4 3 2 1

British Library Cataloguing in Publication Data
A catalogue record for this book is available from the British Library

ISBN 978 1 292 24524 9

Printed in Slovakia by Neografia

Notes from the publisher
1. While the publishers have made every attempt to ensure that advice on the qualifications and its assessment is accurate, the official specification and associated guidance materials are the only authoritative source of information and should always be referred to for definitive guidance. Pearson examiners have not contributed to any sections in this resource relevant to examination papers for which they have responsibility.

2. Pearson has robust editorial processes, including answer and fact checks, to ensure the accuracy of the content in this publication, and every effort is made to ensure this publication is free of errors. We are, however, only human, and occasionally errors do occur. Pearson is not liable for any misunderstandings that arise as a result of errors in this publication, but it is our priority to ensure that the content is accurate. If you spot an error, please do contact us at resourcescorrections@pearson.com so we can make sure it is corrected.

Contents

① Selecting key features

This unit will help you to develop the skills to answer the features question effectively. The skills you will build are how to:

- identify key features
- select supporting detail for key features
- avoid writing too much for key features questions.

In the exam, you will be asked to tackle questions such as the one below. This unit will prepare you to write your own response to this type of question.

Exam-style question

Describe **two** features of government in Elizabethan England.   (4 marks)

Feature 1

....

....

Feature 2

....

....

Remember that relevant key features are things that were characteristic or typical of Elizabethan England – not a single event, such as a minor battle. This means key features are things that were common or happened often, or continued for long periods of time.

The three key questions in the **skills boosts** will help you to answer the features question effectively.

 1 How do I identify a key feature?   **2 How do I select supporting detail?**   **3 How do I ensure I don't include too much supporting detail?**

Read the student's answer to the key features question below and the marker's comments. One mark is awarded for each relevant feature; one mark is awarded for supporting information.

Exam-style question

Describe **two** features of government in Elizabethan England.

(4 marks)

Feature 1

William Cecil is an example of a very important privy councillor. He was very close to Elizabeth I and advised her on important matters. The Privy Council met at least three times a week and advising the monarch was one of its important functions. Although it did not make any decisions itself, it made sure that her final decisions were carried out. The queen had other powers the Privy Council did not, like declaring war.

> This is background material and is irrelevant. You are writing about the Privy Council, not William Cecil.

> Well supported key feature: 2 marks.

> This is focused on the queen; it is not necessary as you have got your 2 marks.

(1) Read the student's answer for Feature 2.

Exam-style question

Feature 2

Justices of the Peace were vital to local government. They reported to the Privy Council and made sure that all social and economic policies were carried out in their areas. Being a JP was a popular role because it was a position of status, although it was unpaid. JPs also heard serious crimes at county courts every three months. They were often gentry, who were near the top of the Elizabethan social hierarchy but below the nobility.

(a) Highlight 🖊 the key feature.

(b) Circle Ⓐ the supporting information.

(c) Cross out ~~cat~~ anything irrelevant.

(d) Draw 🖊 a vertical line (|) at the point in the answer where the student has done enough to get both marks.

Remember this?

The situation on Elizabeth I's accession

This unit uses the theme of the situation on Elizabeth I's accession to build your skills in selecting key features. If you need to review your knowledge of this theme, work through these pages.

1 Draw ✐ lines linking the part of the government to the correct description. There may be more than one relevant description.

part of government	description
A Court	a Approximately 19 advisers who met at least three times a week
	b Could offer advice to the monarch and pass laws
B Privy Council	c Entertained and advised the monarch
	d Granted the monarch extraordinary taxation
	e Heard serious county court cases every three months
C Parliament	f In charge of raising and training county militia
	g Kept law and order locally
D Lords Lieutenant	h Made up of leading courtiers and government advisers
	i Public display of monarch's wealth and power
E Justices of the Peace (JPs)	j Saw all social and economic policies were carried out locally

2 Name ✐ two of the monarch's powers.

1 ....

2 ....

3 Tick ✓ to show whether the following statements are true or false.

		true	false
a	Lords Lieutenant heard the more serious county court cases.	☐	☐
b	William Cecil was Elizabeth I's prime minister.	☐	☐
c	Elizabeth I could set subsidies when she needed more money.	☐	☐
d	Mary, Queen of Scots, was ruling Scotland when Elizabeth I became Queen of England.	☐	☐
e	The only potential husbands of equal status for Elizabeth I were all foreigners.	☐	☐
f	Only the monarch could call and dismiss parliament.	☐	☐

4 Circle (A) the odd one out in each group. Then complete (✐) each sentence to show what the others in the group have in common.

a | Philip II   King Eric of Sweden   Francis II   the Duke of Alençon |

The others were all ....

b | fines   loans   incomes from Crown lands   subsidies |

The others were all ....

c | merchants   gentry   yeomen   tenant farmers |

The others were all ....

5 The three descriptions below all contain inaccuracies. Write (✐) the correct statement under each one.

a Elizabeth I's most important privy councillor was Francis Walsingham, who became Lord Burghley in 1573.

....

....

b Three subjects that Elizabeth I did not want parliament to discuss were vagrancy, her marriage and the succession.

....

....

c The Auld Alliance was the agreement that ended the war between Spain and France in 1559.

....

....

6 Circle (A) which of the following was **not** a function of the Court.

A | To entertain the monarch |

B | To make sure the monarch's decisions were carried out |

C | A public display of wealth and power |

D | To advise the monarch |

7 Circle (A) which of the following was **not** a feature of Roman Catholicism.

A | Belief that the Bible should be in Latin |

B | Belief that there were only two sacraments: Baptism and Holy Communion |

C | The pope was their religious leader |

D | Belief that church services should be in Latin |

How do I identify a key feature?

Key features are things that are typical, clearly recognisable characteristics of a person, place or era in history. This skills boost will help you to identify key features.

Read these two examples of key features of Elizabethan England.

Elizabeth I became queen on 17 November 1558. This is a fact. It might be important, but it is not a key feature. Elizabeth I was a Protestant. This is also a fact. She was a Protestant **for a long time**. It is a **key feature** of Elizabeth I's reign that she was a Protestant.

During Elizabeth I's reign, Drake circumnavigated the globe, from 1577–80. It is a fact. It is one event. It is, however, one of many voyages of exploration that took place. There are **many examples** of voyages of exploration during Elizabeth I's reign. Exploration is a **key feature** of Elizabeth I's reign.

1. Tick ✓ the statements below that you think are key features of Elizabethan England. For those that you select, also tick ✓ the reason why.

	Key feature? ✓	Why? (Long-term trend) ✓	Why? (One of many such examples) ✓
A Elizabeth I's refusal to marry			
B Mary, Queen of Scots, was a danger to Elizabeth I			
C When Elizabeth I became queen, the Crown was £300,000 in debt			
D Scotland was a traditional enemy of England			
E JPs were vital to local government			

2. Read this website extract found by a student during their research and highlight any relevant key features of government in Elizabethan England.

Text 1

When Elizabeth I called parliament in 1572, after the Ridolfi Plot, she was most displeased that they called for the execution of Mary, Queen of Scots. The role of Elizabethan parliaments was to offer advice, not to make demands of the queen. The only time Elizabeth I requested its advice was in the session called from October 1586 to March 1587, when she asked for its view on Mary's execution. Otherwise, parliament was expected simply to pass laws for the queen and grant extraordinary taxation. When Peter Wentworth demanded free speech for MPs in 1576, the Commons itself sent him to the Tower of London.

Is what you have highlighted a key feature?
- Is it something 'typical' of government in Elizabethan England?
- Is it a long-term trend of government in Elizabethan England?

② How do I select supporting detail?

For each key feature, you will get 1 mark for supporting detail. It is important to choose information that is relevant and to avoid including unnecessary description. This skills boost helps you to understand how to select supporting details.

Good supporting details will be:
- relevant to the question
- specific facts or examples
- one of many relevant examples.

① ⓐ A student asked to identify a key feature of Elizabeth I's reign has decided to write about her Privy Council. Choose three statements from the table below that provide good supporting detail on this subject. Tick ✓ the appropriate boxes to explain your choices.

	Relevant ✓	Specific ✓	One of many examples ✓
A The Privy Council met frequently			
B Elizabeth I often chose councillors who were new, Protestant nobles like the Earl of Leicester			
C Sir William Cecil was Elizabeth I's most significant privy councillor			
D The Privy Council played an important part in England's law and order, such as monitoring JPs			
E Elizabeth I's Privy Council had approximately 19 members			
F Elizabeth I often presided over Privy Council meetings			

ⓑ Which of the statements would provide the strongest supporting detail? (Those with the most ticks!) ✏️

....

② A student wrote the following answer to a question asking for two key features of Elizabeth I's Privy Council.

> One key feature of Elizabeth I's Privy Council was its close links to local government. For example, it monitored the work of JPs, who were responsible for implementing the government's social and economic policies, and keeping law and order. JPs were usually large landowners.

ⓐ Highlight ✏️ the supporting detail.

ⓑ Cross out ~~cat~~ any unnecessary description.

3 ## How do I ensure I don't include too much supporting detail?

The key features question is worth 4 marks: 2 marks per key feature. Writing more than you need will not gain you extra marks and will waste time that could be spent tackling the weightier questions. This skills boost will help you judge correctly how much to write for the key features question.

Use the following pieces of advice to write a concise answer.

- Avoid 'filler' material that is irrelevant, unnecessary or contributes nothing of value; this includes background material and descriptions.

- One piece of supporting detail is sufficient. Use it and move on.

- Don't explain the historical terms you use (such as Protestant, vagrancy, succession, colonies). It will be clear from the way they are used whether you understand them.

A student has written an answer to the following exam-style question:

Exam-style question

Describe **two** features of the French threat when Elizabeth I became queen. **(4 marks)**

Feature 1

One key feature was that Mary, Queen of Scots, was also Queen of France. Her mother was Mary of Guise. The Guise were an important, noble, Catholic family that was very powerful and influential in the French court. This meant that the French could threaten England from both north and south at the same time. Mary, Queen of Scots, was Catholic and had a legitimate claim to the English throne, so she could expect support from Catholic France if she pursued her claim.

Feature 2

France and Spain had ended their conflict and signed the Treaty of Cateau-Cambrésis. Spain and France were very powerful countries and traditional enemies. They had been at war during the 1550s and England, under Mary I and Philip II, had sided with Spain. All the while Spain and France were rivals. England was safer, but now there was a real possibility that these two Catholic nations might unite against the Protestant English queen. Protestantism was a Christian religion that rejected a lot of Catholic teaching.

(1) **a** Highlight 🖉 any examples of irrelevant 'filler' material.

b If the student provided two pieces of supporting detail for either key feature, cross out ~~cat~~ the second, unnecessary one.

c Underline Ⓐ any definitions of historical vocabulary.

d Another key feature of the French threat that could have been written about was the Auld Alliance. Write 🖉 your own key feature answer about the Auld Alliance.

Remember: 'Filler' material is unnecessary background information or descriptions that do not directly address the focus of the question.

....

....

....

....

Sample response

Selecting key features and avoiding putting too much detail in your answers is important for any exam question. Once you have made and supported a point, move on. Writing down everything you know is not a skill. The skill is selecting and deploying relevant evidence.

Exam-style question

Describe **two** features of government in Elizabethan England. (4 marks)

Feature 1

Each county had a Lord Lieutenant, usually a member of the nobility and/or Privy Council. They were vital to maintaining the monarch's powers as they oversaw defence and raised local militia. The militia was a force of ordinary people raised in an emergency. Lords Lieutenant were chosen by the monarch to ensure the enforcement of her policies.

Feature 2

The monarch was probably the most important part of the government as she was its head. As a monarch, Elizabeth I was highly intelligent, confident but indecisive. Only the monarch had the power to declare war and make peace. They could rule in some legal cases if the judgement was unclear, or if someone appealed to them, and they could call and dismiss parliament.

① Read the student's response above, then list 🖉 the strengths and weaknesses in the table, using the suggestions below to help you:

Do ...	Don't ...
• give key features rather than an event or one-off occurrence	• add any filler such as background or description
• make sure your key features are relevant	• provide more than one piece of specific supporting detail per feature
• provide specific supporting detail.	• include anything not relevant to the question or key feature.

	Strengths	Weaknesses
Feature 1		
Feature 2		

Your turn!

1. Write 🖊 an answer to the exam-style question below.

Exam-style question

Describe **two** features of society in Elizabethan England.   (4 marks)

Feature 1

....

....

....

....

....

Feature 2

....

....

....

....

....

....

2. Once you have written your answer, identify 🖊 your answer's strengths and weaknesses using the suggestions on page 8.

	Strengths	Weaknesses
Feature 1		
Feature 2		

Review your skills

Check up

Review your response to the exam-style question on page 9. Tick ✓ the column to show how well you think you have done each of the following.

	Had a go ✓	Nearly there ✓	Got it! ✓
identified relevant key features	☐	☐	☐
avoided 'filler' material (description, background, definitions)	☐	☐	☐
selected good supporting detail	☐	☐	☐
written no more than was needed	☐	☐	☐

Look over all of your work in this unit. Note down 🖉 three things you have learned that you will apply when answering key features questions.

① ....

② ....

③ ....

Need more practice?

On separate paper, plan and write 🖉 your response to the exam-style question below.

Exam-style question

Describe **two** features of the reign of Elizabeth I.   (4 marks)

Feature 1

....

....

Feature 2

....

....

How confident do you feel about each of these **skills**? Colour in 🖉 the bars.

❶ How do I identify a key feature?
☐☐☐☐

❷ How do I select supporting detail?
☐☐☐☐

❸ How do I ensure I don't include too much supporting detail?
☐☐☐☐

② Writing strong paragraphs

This unit will help you to develop the skills to write strong paragraphs. The skills you will build are to:

- recognise what makes a strong paragraph
- structure strong paragraphs
- link paragraphs back to the question.

Strong paragraphs are focused and analytical. They have no 'filler' material. You should not write everything you know, but target what you include to focus directly on answering the question. This unit will prepare you to write your own response to questions like the one below, using strong paragraphs.

'Filler' is material that is not relevant to the focus of the question, such as background and unnecessary explanations. Descriptions or narrative with no clear link to the question focus are also unnecessary.

Exam-style question

Explain why there was opposition to the Elizabethan religious settlement 1558–69.

You may use the following in your answer:

- vestments
- the oath of supremacy.

You **must** also use information of your own.

(12 marks)

The three key questions in the **skills boosts** will help you to write strong paragraphs.

1 **How do I focus my paragraphs on answering the question?**

2 **How do I structure a strong paragraph?**

3 **How do I link back to the question?**

Read the following paragraph from a student's response to the exam-style question on page 11.

> One reason for opposition to the Elizabethan religious settlement was that clergy had to wear vestments. Vestments are special clothes worn by the clergy. They were often quite elaborate. Puritans believed this was wrong as it suggested the clergy were special. Puritans were extreme Protestants who wanted to purify the Church of anything Catholic or not in the Bible. Catholics believed priests performed the miracle of transubstantiation during Mass, meaning the bread and wine became the body and blood of Christ, and so were special. Protestants and Puritans thought this was wrong and caused some opposition as the Royal Injunctions said clergy had to wear vestments, but plainer than Catholic ones. Many Puritan clergy refused to wear vestments. Matthew Parker published the 'Book of Advertisements' showing what priests ought to wear and held an exhibition in London. He invited 110 clergy but 37 refused to attend and lost their posts. This shows that although the religious settlement was Protestant, it was still too Catholic for some.

① **a** Cross out (cat) any 'filler' material in the answer.

b Look at the student's planning notes for the next paragraph about opposition to the Elizabethan religious settlement. Place a cross ⊗ alongside any points that are irrelevant to the question.

> A Crucifix controversy = opposition from Puritans because religious settlement too Catholic ☐
>
> B Crucifixes: images of Christ on cross; symbolises Christianity – Christ executed 33CE ☐
>
> C Elizabeth I wanted crucifixes kept, to make churches feel familiar ☐
>
> D Puritans opposed because believed churches should be plain ☐
>
> E Puritans wanted to purify church of Catholicism including ornate decoration, statues of saints ☐
>
> F Puritan bishops opposed the queen, threatened to resign ☐
>
> G Reinforces point that Puritans felt religious settlement too Catholic, so opposed parts of it ☐
>
> H Elizabeth I backing down shows that opposition was too strong sometimes; also not enough Protestant bishops in England to replace bishops who threatened to resign ☐

Remember: Your second paragraph should have:
- an opening sentence that makes the point of the paragraph clear
- a final sentence that links the paragraph back to the question.

The Elizabethan religious settlement

This unit uses the theme of the Elizabethan religious settlement to build your skills in writing strong paragraphs. If you need to review your knowledge of this theme, work through these pages.

1. Complete (✐) this table about the three parts of the Elizabethan religious settlement.

What it was	What it did
Act of Supremacy	
Act of Uniformity	
Royal Injunctions	*Reinforced the Acts of Supremacy and Uniformity.* Features of the Royal Injunctions: 1 2 3

2. Draw (✐) lines linking each of the counties/cities below to a description, according to how Catholic or Protestant it was.

A Durham		a Strongly Catholic
B Essex		
C Kent		b Some Catholic support
D Lancashire		
E London		c Some Protestant support
F Suffolk		d Strongly Protestant

3. Write (✐) 'P' or 'C' in the box to say whether the following are key features of Protestantism or Catholicism.

a Transubstantiation ☐

b Two sacraments ☐

c The Church can forgive sins ☐

d People have their own relationship with God ☐

e Pilgrimages ☐

f Ornaments ☐

g Bible and services in your own language ☐

h Miracles ☐

4 Name 🖉 one way in which Puritans differed from other Protestants.

....

....

5 Write 🖉 the numbers 1–6 in the boxes to put the following events in chronological order.

A	Attempting to convert people to Catholicism became treason	☐
B	Catholic priests first smuggled into England from abroad	☐
C	First visitations	☐
D	Revolt of the Northern Earls	☐
E	Papal bull	☐
F	Pope's instructions to Catholics not to attend Church of England services	☐

6 Choose the correct answer from the choices in the box below. 🖉

| 20 shillings | 1 shilling | recusant | traitors | 2,000 | 8,000 | 1 | 27 |

a What was the name for a Catholic who did not attend Church of England services?

....

b How many English priests took the oath of supremacy to Elizabeth I?

....

c What was the fine for not going to church on a Sunday or holy day?

....

d How many English bishops refused to take the oath of supremacy to Elizabeth I?

....

7 Circle Ⓐ which of the following were **not** part of visitations. (There is more than one answer.)

A	Preaching licences were checked
B	Holy Communion wine-tasting
C	Ensuring everyone had taken the oath of supremacy
D	All clergy had to sit examinations on the new Book of Common Prayer

8 Circle Ⓐ which of the following was a cause of the Revolt of the Northern Earls in 1569.

A	A desire to restore Catholicism
B	The earls had lost influence at court
C	France and Spain had promised to support the rebellion
D	A plan to marry Mary, Queen of Scots, to the Duke of Norfolk

How do I focus my paragraphs on answering the question?

Students often write down everything they know in an answer for fear of missing something out. Strong paragraphs, however, are focused and analytical. This skills boost will help you to identify the key features of a strong paragraph.

Here are a student's notes for an answer to the exam-style question on page 11 on why there was opposition to the Elizabethan religious settlement 1558–69.

A Catholic opposition; England: majority = Catholic, especially North and West England

B Papacy opposed Elizabethan religious settlement – considered Protestantism to be heresy

C Heretics = people who deny the Catholic Church

D 1566: Pope instructed English Catholics not to go to Church of England services → recusants

E Recusants were Catholics who refused to go to Church of England services

F Elizabeth I wanted to keep churches looking familiar to reduce Catholic opposition, e.g. by keeping crucifixes

G Keeping crucifixes led to Protestant opposition as it was too Catholic

H Queen liked crucifixes: two in Royal Chapel; Elizabeth I wanted them to be kept in churches

(1) Highlight ✐ only the information in the notes above that is **necessary** to answer the essay question.

It is not necessary to explain historical words or terms in an essay unless they are in the title. Your understanding will be clear from how you use them. Read the paragraph below.

There was Catholic opposition to the Elizabethan Protestant religious settlement on several points. One was the miracle that Catholics believed took place during Mass, when the bread and wine became the body and blood of Christ. For Protestants, this was simply a reminder of the last time Christ shared bread and wine with his disciples. Another point was cutting the number of church services in which there was a holy presence that gave God's blessing from seven to two: Protestants only recognised Baptism and Holy Communion. There was also opposition to the oath accepting Elizabeth I as the Governor of the Church. In 1558 England's bishops were all Catholic and only one took the oath. After the first inspections to make sure the Elizabethan religious settlement was being followed, 400 clergy were dismissed, though not all were Catholic.

(2) Cross out ⟨cat⟩ the explanation/description in the paragraph above and write ✐ in the letter of the term from the list below that could be used instead.

A | The Last Supper

B | The sacraments

C | The oath of supremacy

D | Transubstantiation

E | Visitations

2 How do I structure a strong paragraph?

When starting a paragraph, don't 'set the scene' with extra background information that is irrelevant to the question. Begin with a point about the question that the paragraph is answering. The main body should be focused and concise, with no 'filler'. End with a link back to the question. This skills boost will help you to structure a strong paragraph.

A good opening sentence provides a clear link to the question by making a point about it.

(1) Tick ✓ which of the following would make the best start to a paragraph about why there was Protestant opposition to the religious settlement

A | Puritans wanted to purify the Church from any Catholic, or 'popish', opposition. | ☐

B | There was Protestant opposition to the religious settlement as some found it too Catholic. | ☐

C | Elizabeth I wanted her religious settlement to be acceptable to Catholics and Protestants. | ☐

Here are some statements that a student included in a paragraph on the vestments controversy:

> *a* Puritans are Protestants who follow the Bible very strictly indeed.
> *b* Puritans objected to Elizabeth I's command that priests wear vestments, because special clothing implied that they were different from their congregation.
> *c* Vestments are special, elaborate clothing worn by priests.
> *d* Catholics, unlike Protestants, believed in the miracle of transubstantiation during Mass.
> *e* By 1566, it was clear that not all clergy were following services properly or wearing vestments.
> *f* In 1566, Matthew Parker set out further guidelines for priests in his 'Book of Advertisements'.
> *g* Matthew Parker called 110 Puritan priests to an exhibition of vestments but 37 refused, and left their posts in the Church rather than obey the religious settlement.

The student started their essay with statement **A**, then used statements **a–g** in their paragraph.

(2) Why is statement A not a good way to start the paragraph? ✐

....

....

....

(3) Use the table below to evaluate the statements the student has chosen. ✓

Which statements ...	a ✓	b ✓	c ✓	d ✓	e ✓	f ✓	g ✓
have **unnecessary** description?							
are **not** focused on the question?							

(4) Which **four** statements would you use for the paragraph? Choose an introductory sentence from **(1)**, followed by three from **a–g**. ✐ ....

3 How do I link back to the question?

To link your answer back to the question, you need to refer to the key points in it. Include some of its key words and phrases in each paragraph opening. End each paragraph with a clear judgement that is justified by referring back to the key words from the question. This skills boost will help you to link your paragraphs back to the question.

Here is a student's plan for the main body of an essay to answer the exam-style question on page 11.

Paragraph 1:

Royal Supremacy = key cause of opposition; for Catholics pope = head of Church, God's only representative on Earth. Catholic Church = hierarchy: under pope were cardinals, archbishops, bishops, archdeacons, priests. Bishops all Catholic so only one took oath BUT majority of priests did take it. Protestants didn't believe in popes, no real opposition despite Elizabeth's gender. So Royal Supremacy led to great opposition but only from Catholic bishops; much less from lower clergy.

Paragraph 2:

Appearance of churches and clergy → opposition. Puritans wanted simple churches, Elizabeth I thought crucifixes important to reassure Catholics. Royal Supremacy meant she was head of Church, so could keep crucifixes. Catholics liked decorated churches. Some Puritan bishops threatened to resign. They'd been in the Netherlands, where Protestantism was strong. Not enough Protestant bishops → position of strength as Elizabeth I needed Puritans and had to give in to their opposition.

The student then wrote the following paragraph based on the plan for paragraph 1.

One reason for opposition to the religious settlement was that clergy had to take an oath agreeing to the Royal Supremacy. For Catholics, the only spiritual leader was the pope, God's representative on Earth. So, this part of the settlement was a step too far. England's bishops were all Catholic when Elizabeth I became queen. All but one refused the oath. Although most of the lower clergy were also Catholic, the majority took it. Protestants did not believe there should be a pope, so it was not an issue for them. So, the Royal Supremacy led to some opposition but nothing that seriously affected it.

1. In the student's paragraph above:

   a. underline Ⓐ where the student has made the point of the paragraph clear

   b. double underline Ⓐ the explanation of the point of the paragraph

   c. circle Ⓐ any evidence supporting the explanation

   d. cross out (eat) any 'filler' material or irrelevancies

   Look at the plan: was there any 'filler'? Did the student make the mistake of including it?

   e. highlight 🖊 clear links to the question focus, demonstrated by the use of key words from the question.

2. Identify the focus of the second paragraph and write 🖊 it on a separate piece of paper.

3. Look at the plan for paragraph 2. Highlight 🖊 only those parts that are necessary to write a strong paragraph.

Sample response

Strong, focused, analytical paragraphs with clear links back to the question are an important part of any written examination.

Read the following extracts from an answer to the exam-style question on page 11.

Paragraph 1

It is hard to identify Catholic opposition to the religious settlement before 1569, as Elizabeth I did not want recusants punished. She wanted Catholicism to die out. Recusants are Catholics who refused to attend Church of England services. Early punishments were lenient: a fine of one shilling for non-attendance. There was clearly some Catholic opposition at first, as all but one bishop refused to take the oath of supremacy to Elizabeth I as head of the Church in 1559. At that time, all the bishops were Catholics from Mary's reign. Some lesser clergy refused to take the oath, but about 8,000 did out of 10,000 parishes in England. So a large majority of lesser clergy took the oath. There was opposition because of religious divisions in England too, with the North and West being more Catholic and London, Kent and East Anglia being more Protestant.

Paragraph 2

There was serious opposition in northern England because much of it remained strongly Catholic. It is not possible to say that it was all about religion, but it was a protest against the religious settlement for the ordinary people taking part. The new Bishop of Durham, James Pilkington, a strict Protestant, was very unpopular. The rebels carried Catholic banners and held Mass in Durham. The rebellion's leaders were northern earls from ancient Catholic families. However, they had other reasons for rebelling. They resented newcomers at court, like Leicester or Cecil who had much more influence than them. So there were reasons other than religion for the Revolt of the Northern Earls.

(1) Write 🖉 '1' and/or '2' in the table to identify the strengths and weaknesses of paragraphs 1 and 2.

Strengths		Weaknesses	
Paragraph opens with a clear point about why there was opposition.		Paragraph contains information that is unnecessary or irrelevant (filler).	
Paragraph ends with a clear link back to the question.		Paragraph wanders off the question focus.	
A reason why there was opposition is clearly explained with relevant evidence.		Paragraph contains unnecessary explanation of historical terms.	

(2) Overall, how well do you think the student answers the question? Draw 🖉 an arrow below to show your choice. Give 🖉 the student one piece of advice to help them improve their answer.

1/6	2/6	3/6	4/6	5/6	6/6
No focus. Question not answered.	Poor. Largely without focus.	More unfocused than focused.	More focused than not.	Good answer. Well focused.	Excellent. Focused throughout.

Your turn!

(1) Rewrite ✏️ the two paragraphs from the sample answer so that they give a more focused answer, with clear links back to the question. The sample answer is 246 words; try to write your answer in fewer than 200 words. Use the following prompts to help you.

Checklist	✓
Does your opening statement say what cause / consequence / change / feature the paragraph is addressing?	
Is your answer focused? Avoid 'filler' material.	
Does your answer provide support for your explanation of the cause / consequence / change / feature you are writing about?	
Does your last statement link back to the question: • How important is this cause / consequence / change / feature? • Is this cause / consequence / change / feature more or less important than the stated cause / consequence / change / feature?	
Is the question wording in your answer?	

Exam-style question

Why was there opposition to the Elizabethan religious settlement 1558–69?

You may use the following in your answer:

• vestments
• the oath of supremacy.

You **must** also use information of your own.

(12 marks)

Review your skills

Check up

Review your response to the exam-style question on page 19. Tick ✓ the column to show how well you think you have done each of the following.

	Had a go ✓	Nearly there ✓	Got it! ✓
opened each paragraph with a clear point about the question	☐	☐	☐
ended each paragraph with a clear link back to the question, avoiding any 'filler'	☐	☐	☐
used historical terms without explaining them or describing what they mean	☐	☐	☐

Look over all of your work in this unit. Note down ✏ three things you have learned that you will apply when writing strong paragraphs.

① ....

② ....

③ ....

Need more practice?

On separate paper, plan and write ✏ your response to the exam-style question below.

Exam-style question

Explain why Anglo-Spanish relations deteriorated in the years 1571–81.

You may use the following in your answer:

• the Ridolfi Plot (1571)
• Francis Drake knighted (1581).

You **must** also use information of your own.

(12 marks)

How confident do you feel about each of these **skills**? Colour ✏ in the bars.

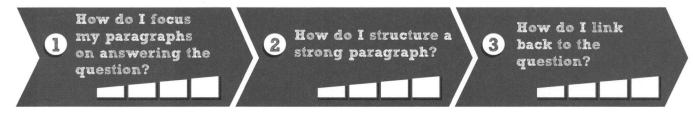

1 How do I focus my paragraphs on answering the question?

2 How do I structure a strong paragraph?

3 How do I link back to the question?

(3) Analysing causation

This unit will help you to develop the skills to analyse causation effectively. The skills you will build are how to:

- build causal arguments
- develop causal arguments
- link causal arguments to the question.

In the exam, you will be asked to tackle questions such as the one below. This unit will prepare you to write your own response to this type of question.

Exam-style question

Explain why vagrancy increased in Elizabethan England in the years 1558–88.

You may use the following in your answer:

- population growth
- sheep farming.

You **must** also include information of your own.

(12 marks)

The three key questions in the **skills boosts** will help you understand how to analyse causation effectively.

(1) How do I build a causal argument?

(2) How do I develop a causal argument?

(3) How do I link causal arguments to the question?

Below are two students' plans for the following exam-style question:

Exam-style question

Explain why vagrancy increased in Elizabethan England in the years 1558–88.

You may use the following in your answer:

- population growth
- sheep farming.

You **must** also include information of your own.

(12 marks)

Plan A

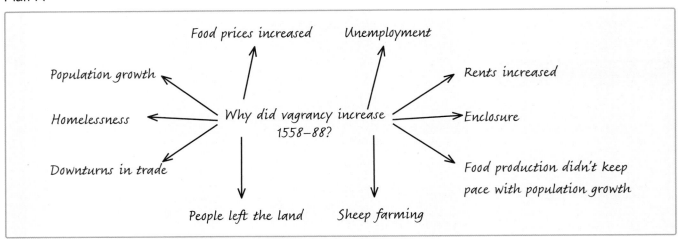

Plan B

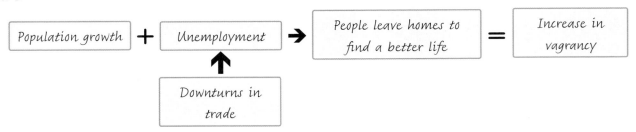

① Evaluate 🖉 these plans using the table below by writing 'A' or 'B' in the appropriate box.

How well does each plan ...	Very well	Quite well	Not at all
show a wide variety of reasons?			
show how one cause leads to another, and so on?			
show how causes interact with each other?			

The problem of the poor

This unit uses the theme of the problem of the poor to build your skills in analysing causation. If you need to review your knowledge of this theme, work through these pages.

1 Circle Ⓐ the factors below that were **not** a consequence of population growth.

A Increased food prices	**B** Falling food prices	**C** A rise in unemployment
D A fall in unemployment	**E** Wages reduced	**F** Wages increased
G Rents went up	**H** Rents went down	

2 Tick ✓ whether the following statements are true or false.

		true	false
a	The idle (undeserving) poor were treated more harshly than the impotent (deserving) poor.	☐	☐
b	A vagrant, or vagabond, was someone without a home who wandered the country begging.	☐	☐
c	Unemployment fell when there was a downturn in the cloth trade.	☐	☐
d	All vagrants were thrown in gaol.	☐	☐
e	Elizabethans thought unemployment was simply laziness.	☐	☐
f	Ipswich had a school for poor children and a hospital for the poor and sick.	☐	☐
g	Elizabethans often gave vagrants money and sent them on their way rather than arrest them.	☐	☐

3 Draw ✏ lines to match the features to the Acts of Parliament.

features   **Acts of Parliament**

features	Acts of Parliament
A Established national poor rate for the first time	**a** 1563 Statute of Artificers
B Those who refused to work were sent to a house of correction	
C JPs were to keep a register of the poor	
D Anyone who refused to pay poor rates could be imprisoned	**b** 1572 Vagabonds Act
E Towns and cities had to find work for the able-bodied poor	
F Set increasingly harsh punishments for those found guilty of vagrancy – the third time led to the death penalty	**c** 1576 Poor Relief Act

4 What was the difference between poor relief and the poor rate? ✏

....

....

....

5 Statements **a–e** below are steps leading from **A** (an increase in the demand for wool) to **B** (an increase in vagrancy). Write 🖊 the letters in the boxes in the correct order to show how **A** led to **B**.

| **A** Population growth increased demand for wool. | ▷ | ▷ | ▷ | ▷ | ▷ | **B** There was an increase in vagrancy. |

a Rural depopulation as people went in search of work

b There was an increase in sheep farming

c Wages fell

d Rural unemployment rose

e Less labour was needed to farm sheep

6 Draw 🖊 lines to match the terms with the descriptions.

A Up and down husbandry	**a** Growing enough to feed the family but not to sell
B Subsistence farming	**b** Growing crops
C Entry fee	**c** Land used for crops one year, livestock the next
D Arable	**d** Cost of taking over a piece of land

7 For each group below, circle Ⓐ the odd one out and say 🖊 why it is the odd one out.

a | Cloth trade 1563–64   Cloth trade 1568–73   Cloth trade 1579–83   Cloth trade 1586–88 |

It is the odd one out because ....

b | register for the poor   providing unemployed with raw materials
drilling holes in vagrants' ears   national poor rate |

It is the odd one out because ....

c | impotent   vagrants   itinerants   idle |

It is the odd one out because ....

d | under 16   skilled labour   over 80   widows |

It is the odd one out because ....

8 Tick ☑ the response which best describes how modern historians sometimes define 'the poor' of Elizabethan England.

A People who couldn't afford to eat meat more than once a month. ☐

B People who earned less than 10 shillings a week. ☐

C People who spent 80% of their income on bread. ☐

1 How do I build a causal argument?

Causal arguments look at series of causes that build up to bring about a specific problem or situation. This skills boost will help you to build a causal argument.

Here are some evidence cards concerning why vagrancy increased 1558–88:

A Food prices increased	**B** Wages decreased	**C** Downturns in trade	**D** Sheep more profitable

K Population increased rapidly

Why did vagrancy increase 1558–88?

E Shortage of land

J Enclosure

F Shortage of food as production didn't match population growth

I Shortage of jobs (unemployment)

H Rents increased

G People left countryside

1 **a** Pick any three from cards A–K and write ✏ them in column 2 of the table.

1 Caused by ...	2 Card chosen	Resulting in ...
		increased vagrancy

b Identify any cards that caused your three choices. Write ✏ them in column 1 (Caused by ...). If one of your choices does not have any causes, leave the cell beside it in column 1 blank.

2 Causal arguments must be made in a logical order, showing how one cause led to another until the outcome was reached. Using the evidence cards above, complete ✏ these two flow diagrams to make a logical sequence of causation.

a

☐ ➔ **I** ➔ ☐ ➔ **G** ➔ Increase in vagrancy

b

K ➔ ☐ ➔ **D** ➔ ☐ ➔ **G** ➔ Increase in vagrancy

How do I develop a causal argument?

When you write causal arguments, it is important to avoid making them read like lists. This skills boost will help you to write developed causal arguments.

Students were asked to use the flow diagram below to write two paragraphs explaining why vagrancy increased in the years 1558–88.

Paragraph A

There was more unemployment because the population grew. Vagrancy increased as people lost their homes, causing them to wander the countryside. Without work they couldn't afford their rents leading to vagrancy.

Paragraph B

Secondly, the shortage of jobs caused wages to fall. Employers could pay less because there were plenty of unemployed people willing to take any work they could get. Falling wages often resulted in severe poverty, meaning people consequently could not afford their rents, leading to homelessness. A direct consequence of this was that people ended up wandering the countryside or heading to cities hoping for a better life.

(1) In paragraphs A and B, highlight ✎ the words and phrases used to build a causal argument.

Words and phrases used to build causal arguments
caused   because   consequently/consequence of in turn   leading/led to   resulted in

(2) What are the strengths and weaknesses of the two paragraphs? Complete ✎ the table below with the appropriate paragraph letter.

Strengths	A, B or both?	Weaknesses	A, B or both?
Clear focus to the paragraph		Paragraph focus uncertain	
Causation is explained		A series of statements about cause	
Specific supporting evidence		Undeveloped historical knowledge	

An important part of developing a causal argument is supporting it with evidence.

(3) Using some of the linking phrases from (1) and your own words, complete ✎ the sequence below.

England's population grew by 35% during Elizabeth I's reign ....

.... the supply of labour to increase. ....

.... unemployment and vagrancy grew worse, for example

when the cloth trade was bad in 1568–73 it .... the government passing the 1572 Vagabonds Act.

3 How do I link causal arguments to the question?

Linking causal arguments back to the question is important to make sure you don't wander from the question focus. This skills boost will help you understand how to do that.

It is important to reason through from your start point to your end point and stay focused. Look at this list of factors that could be included in the answer to the question on page 21.

| A Population increased | B Food prices increased | C Increased demand for wool |

| D Rents increased | E Wages decreased | F Rural depopulation | G Enclosure |

| H Evictions | I Sheep more profitable | J Demand for labour fell | K Unemployment |

Using the factors listed above, the flow chart below shows a paragraph plan to explain how an increase in the population led to an increased demand for wool, which eventually led to rural depopulation.

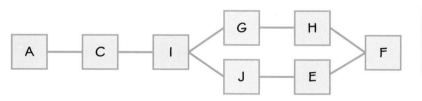

There may be many possible factors leading to an event. Ranking them by importance will ensure you select the ones that you can explain most effectively.

1 Study the evidence below then underline (A) three factors in the list above that you think had the greatest impact on vagrancy.

| 2–3% of land was enclosed. | As the demand for land rose, so did rents. |

| Some families spent 80% of their income on bread. | Prices rose faster than wages. |

2 Put ✎ your underlined causes in order of importance, according to how effectively you think you can explain them.

A student using the paragraph plan above has decided that the most important cause of vagrancy shown was rural depopulation, and its most important causes were rising rents and falling wages. At the end of their analysis, they need to link back to the question to explain why. Having ranked the factors by importance and chosen those with the greatest impact, they need an effective final sentence that:

• summarises the chain of causes
• ends the chain with the key idea/words from the question.

3 Tick ✓ which of the following final sentences best links the causal argument back to the question on page 21.

| A | So, increasing the demand for wool, making sheep more profitable, caused the merging of some small farms and rising rents, which, as the demand for labour fell, led to wages decreasing, causing evictions and rural depopulation, and leading to vagrancy. | ☐ |

| B | Population growth therefore led to vagrancy by causing pressure that led to rural depopulation, as many people left the land after losing their homes and jobs. | ☐ |

| C | This shows that population growth caused vagrancy. | ☐ |

Sample response

Careful planning is important to ensure that you produce an effective causal argument with a clear progression towards your final explanation of the issue in the question.

Study the plans below that students have written in response to the exam-style question on page 21.

Plan A: Paragraph 1

Population growth of up to 35% led to:

(a) More labour → lower wages and more unemployment (both in countryside and town)

(b) And at same time → wages decreased AND → more pressure on food as production didn't keep pace → higher prices AND → higher rents. So cost of living rose as wages fell. Thus population growth → poverty through too much labour and not enough land, food.

Paragraph 2:

Trade also **important cause** of poverty as downturns → more unemployment → more poverty: woollen cloth = 81.6% England's exports: 1563–64; 1568–73; 1586–88; impact seen in Acts of Parliament (e.g. 1563 Statute of Artificers ensured poor relief collected; 1572 Vagabonds Act – unemployment = real problem for first time). So unemployment and thus poverty worsened further at these times.

Paragraph 3:

Enclosure = worry for people as could lead to eviction if small farms merged; plus fewer jobs farming sheep led to unemployment and also led to poverty and eviction led to vagabondage

Plan B: Paragraph 1

Population grew by up to 35% → increased food prices as food production didn't keep pace.

Paragraph 2:

Population grew → increased labour supply → more unemployment. Statute of Artificers ensured poor relief collected; 1572 Vagabonds Act – unemployment seen as real problem for first time. 1576 Poor Relief Act provided work for unemployed.

Paragraph 3:

Population grew → more pressure on land → rents rose → poverty → vagrancy

Paragraph 4:

Sheep farming more profitable → enclosure → small farms merging → eviction; plus needed less labour so → unemployment

Paragraph 5:

When trade bad, unemployment rose e.g. 1563–64; 1568–73; 1586–88; led to Acts of Parliament: Statute of Artificers ensured poor relief collected; 1572 Vagabonds Act – unemployment seen as real problem for first time; 1576 Poor Relief Act provided work for unemployed.

To develop a causal argument, you need to:
- clearly show causation
- combine causation with evidence
- link back to the question
- highlight other important causes.

① Which do you think is the better plan and why?

....

....

....

....

Your turn!

Now it's your turn to try and answer an exam-style question.

Exam-style question

Explain why vagrancy increased in Elizabethan England in the years 1558–88.

You may use the following in your answer:

- population growth
- sheep farming.

You **must** also include information of your own.

(12 marks)

① Use the words and phrases from page 26 to write up one of the paragraphs from plan A on page 28.

Remember to use factual evidence to develop and support your argument.

....

....

....

....

....

....

....

....

....

....

....

....

....

....

....

....

....

....

....

....

....

....

Review your skills

Check up

Review your response to the exam-style question on page 29. Tick ✓ the column to show how well you think you have done each of the following.

	Had a go ✓	Nearly there ✓	Got it! ✓
built a causal argument	☐	☐	☐
developed the causal argument effectively	☐	☐	☐
linked the causal argument to the question	☐	☐	☐

Look over all of your work in this unit. Note down ✏ three things you have learned that you will apply when analysing causation.

① ....

② ....

③ ....

Need more practice?

On separate paper, plan and write ✏ your response to the exam-style question below.

Exam-style question

Explain why Elizabeth I faced challenges both at home and abroad in the years 1558–68.

You may use the following in your answer:

• the religious settlement
• Mary, Queen of Scots' arrival in England (1568).

You **must** also use information of your own.

(12 marks)

How confident do you feel about each of these **skills**? Colour ✏ in the bars.

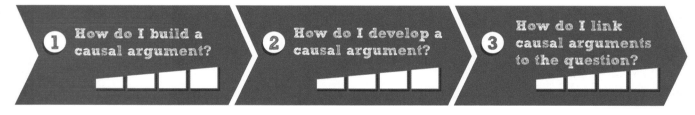

① How do I build a causal argument?

② How do I develop a causal argument?

③ How do I link causal arguments to the question?

 ④ Evaluating cause in context

Understanding cause requires understanding its context. This unit will help you to evaluate change in context. The skills you will build are how to:

- identify the features of context that are relevant
- show the influence of context
- evaluate the importance of context.

In the exam, you will be asked to tackle questions such as the one below. This unit will prepare you to write your own response to this type of question.

Exam-style question

'The main reason why Mary, Queen of Scots, was executed was her claim to the English throne.'

How far do you agree? Explain your answer.

You may use the following in your answer:

- Spanish invasion plans
- the Babington Plot.

You **must** also use information of your own.

(16 marks)

What is context?

Context can be defined as the circumstances or setting in which events happen. Events can have a political, economic, social or religious context, for example, as well as an international and domestic context.

The three key questions in the **skills boosts** will help you understand how to evaluate cause in context.

 How do I identify the features of context that are relevant?

 How do I show the influence of context?

 How do I evaluate the importance of context?

Being able to describe the context in which historical figures acted and against which historical events took place can be very helpful in explaining why people reacted in a certain way or why circumstances changed in the way that they did.

1 Draw ✎ lines linking the contexts (situations) and the terms that could be applied to describe them.

For example: **B** economics → **c** (growth, boom, recession, downturn) or **A** politics → **b** (extremist, moderate) and **d** (conservative, radical)

context	terms
A politics	a stable, unstable, volatile
	b extremist, moderate
B economics	c growth, boom, recession, downturn
C society	d conservative, radical
	e strong, weak
D religion	f peace, war
E international relations	g wealth, employment, poverty, unemployment

It is also possible to make predictions about what outcomes might result from a specific context.

2 Draw ✎ lines to match each context to its possible outcomes.

context	could lead to ...
A Unstable political situation	a revolution
B Economic boom	b war
C Extremist religious beliefs	c persecution of minorities
D Volatile international relations	d rejection of any change
E Conservative social attitudes	e rapid social progress
F Poverty	f social tension
G Peaceful international situation	g improved trade
H Radical politics	h dictatorship

Plots and revolts

This unit uses the theme of plots and revolts to build your skills in evaluating cause in context. If you need to review your knowledge of this theme, work through these pages.

1 Give 🖉 two reasons why Mary, Queen of Scots, was a threat to Elizabeth I.

....

....

2 Write 🖉 the following events against the correct dates in the chronological list below.

| Babington Plot | Ridolfi Plot | Spanish Armada | Mary, Queen of Scots' arrival in England |

| Papal bull of excommunication | Throckmorton Plot | Execution of Mary, Queen of Scots |

| Catholic priests began arriving in England | Revolt of the Northern Earls |

1568 .... 1569–70 .... 1570 ....

1571 .... 1574 .... 1583–84 ....

1586 .... 1587 .... 1588 ....

3 Circle Ⓐ the odd one out in each group. Why is it the odd one out? 🖉

a | Revolt of the Northern Earls　　Ridolfi Plot　　Throckmorton Plot　　Babington Plot |

It is the odd one out because ....

....

b | Westmorland　　Northumberland　　Norfolk　　Sussex |

It is the odd one out because ....

....

c | ciphers　　wiretapping　　*agents provocateurs*　　torture |

It is the odd one out because ....

....

d | Neville　　Cecil　　Howard　　Percy |

It is the odd one out because ....

....

e | Duke of Guise　　Duke of Norfolk　　Philip II of Spain　　Duke of Alba |

It is the odd one out because ....

....

Unit 4 Evaluating cause in context　　33

4 Which of A–G below were parts of which plots? Complete 🖉 the table by writing the correct letters in the correct column. Some letters might belong in more than one column.

Ridolfi Plot, 1571	Throckmorton Plot, 1583–84	Babington Plot, 1586

A | Philip II would supply 10,000 soldiers from the Netherlands.

B | Letters written in code were sent to Mary, Queen of Scots, about the plot.

C | Norfolk was involved in the plot.

D | Catholics were prepared to assassinate Elizabeth I.

E | The French Duke of Guise would invade England and free his cousin, Mary, Queen of Scots.

F | The Duke of Guise would supply 60,000 men.

G | Spain, France and the pope supported this plot.

5 Briefly explain 🖉 how the Act for the Preservation of the Queen's Safety (1585) helped lead to Mary, Queen of Scots' execution.

....

....

....

....

6 Circle Ⓐ which of the following were **not** consequences of the Revolt of the Northern Earls.

A | The relaxing of the religious settlement

B | The execution of the Duke of Norfolk

C | The execution of the Earl of Westmorland

D | A Protestant (the Earl of Huntingdon) was sent to lead the Council of the North.

7 Circle Ⓐ which of the following were used by the Catholic Church to oppose Elizabeth I.

A | Protest marches in 1580–82

B | The papal bull of 1570

C | A blockade of English ports in 1579

D | The smuggling of Catholic priests into England from Europe after 1574

8 Circle Ⓐ which of the following were consequences of the Throckmorton Plot.

A | 11,000 Catholics imprisoned/under surveillance

B | Law passed making sheltering Catholic priests punishable by death

C | An increase in the fine for recusancy to £20

D | The torture and execution of Francis Throckmorton

1 How do I identify the features of context that are relevant?

Context can help to explain why the same person reacts to the same problem in different ways at different times. A difference in the situation, or in the events leading up to it, can produce different outcomes. This skills boost will help you identify the relevant features of context.

Look back to the exam-style question on page 31. Why was Mary, Queen of Scots, executed in 1587 when she had been in England since 1568 and there had been other, arguably more serious plots, since 1568?

A student made the following notes:

Religious context 1560s	1570s	1580s
England = Protestant; large portion of population = Catholic	No change	

Political context 1560s	1570s	1580s
Mary = Catholic with strong claim to English throne	No change	
Mary captive in England	No change	
Plots against Elizabeth I – Revolt of the Northern Earls 1569–70	Plots continued but less serious (Ridolfi)	

International context 1560s	1570s	1580s
Anglo-Spanish relations = tense	No change; still tense	
Spain and France = rivals	No change	
England intervening unofficially in the Netherlands	No change	

(1) Think about the following events of the 1580s:

[Throckmorton Plot] [Treaty of Joinville] [Treaty of Nonsuch]

[Drake's voyages: circumnavigation] [Philip II began building the Armada] [Babington Plot]

Did they cause the context to change in 1587? How? Complete ✏ the table for the 1580s.

(2) Explain ✏ why Mary, Queen of Scots, was a greater threat in 1587 than she had been in 1568. Use the changes in context in your completed table to inform your answer.

....

....

....

....

2 How do I show the influence of context?

If you are looking to explain an event, remember to consider context alongside the other causes. Does it change? Has it influenced other developments leading to the event? This skills boost will help you to show the influence of context.

The notes below were made by a student looking at why Mary, Queen of Scots, was executed in 1587. Her notes focus on reviewing developments in the situation: how England's Catholics were treated as an indication of how great the Catholic threat was.

- 1569–70: execution of approx. 450 rebels after Revolt of the Northern Earls
- 1571: Act of Parliament widens definition of treason to include calling Elizabeth I a heretic and bringing in or printing papal bulls
- 1581: new, harsher laws against Catholics – fine for recusancy increased to £20; attempting to convert people to Catholicism became treason
- 1583: government's reaction to Throckmorton Plot more wide-ranging than before: 11,000 Catholics imprisoned/under surveillance
- 1585: Act of Parliament makes sheltering Catholic priests punishable by death
- 1586–87: Babington → mass arrests of Catholics and 31 priests and Mary, Queen of Scots, executed

(1) What do you notice about the changes in how Catholics were treated in England?

....

(2) Review the student's notes above. Beside each date in the table below, write the change in context that was also happening and which may have led to changes in the treatment of Catholics.

Date	Change in context
1569	
1571	
1581	
1585	
1586–87	

Now assess how changing context can lead to different events and outcomes and how that links to the question. Study the student answer extract below and answer (3) to demonstrate this.

> The treatment of English Catholics in the 1580s shows that Elizabeth I felt the Catholic threat had intensified. Domestically not much had changed. Although there were the Throckmorton and Babington plots, laws against Catholics became harsher before then, in 1581. Also, the Revolt of the Northern Earls was more serious, so the harsher treatment can't only be down to the plots. Instead it coincides with a changing international context. … This played an important part in the change in the Catholic threat in the 1580s.

(3) Write 2–3 sentences that could fill the gap in the student's paragraph above, explaining how the international context changed. ....

....

....

③ How do I evaluate the importance of context?

There will always be a context for events, but it is not always significant. This skills boost will help you to determine the significance of context.

A good way to evaluate the importance of the context of an event is to ask:

? Why did the event happen then? Why not sooner/later? What changed?

① Use the table to test whether changing context can explain Mary's execution. For each description of context, tick ✓ whether it was present in the 1560s and/or 1580s. If both columns have been ticked, there is no change. If there has been no change, it cannot help explain Mary's execution.

Domestic context	1560s ✓	1580s ✓
Elizabeth I and religious settlement = Protestant		
Pope = alternative source of authority for English Catholics		
Mary, Queen of Scots, captive in England; strong claim to throne		
Catholic plots failed		
International context	**1560s ✓**	**1580s ✓**
All of the Netherlands was rebelling against Spanish rule		
A large Spanish army was in the Netherlands		
Spain and France were rivals		
Philip II was planning to invade England		

② **a** You now need to assess the significance of this context. How significant was the domestic context by 1587 to explain why Mary, Queen of Scots, was executed? Write ✏ your score and then explain it.
Use these scores:

1 = highly significant   2 = very significant   3 = quite significant   4 = not at all significant

Score: ⬚ ....

....

b How significant was the international context by 1587 to explain why Mary, Queen of Scots, was executed? Write ✏ your score then explain it.

Score: ⬚ ....

....

③ How far does the changing context explain Mary as a growing threat to Elizabeth I in the years 1558–88? Draw ✏ an arrow below to show your answer.

100% Mary	Largely Mary	More Mary than context	More context than Mary	Largely context	100% context
┃	┃	┃	┃	┃	┃

④ Write ✏ an introduction to the exam-style question on page 31. Write 2–3 sentences, explaining how the change in context led to Mary, Queen of Scots' execution. Continue on paper if you need to.

....

....

Sample response

Being able to identify and evaluate context is a useful skill that can help you to explain historical events.

Exam-style question

'The main reason why Mary, Queen of Scots, was executed was her claim to the throne.'

How far do you agree? Explain your answer.

You may use the following in your answer:

- Spanish invasion plans
- the Babington Plot.

You **must** also use information of your own.

(16 marks)

This extract is from one student's answer to the exam-style question above.

If Mary, Queen of Scots' claim to the throne had been the reason for her execution, then she would have been executed much earlier. For example, Norfolk was a threat to the throne and was executed after the Ridolfi Plot, but Mary was not. The Ridolfi Plot involved the Spanish and had papal approval. The pope had issued his papal bull against Elizabeth I the year before. This made all English Catholics suspect, thus changing the domestic context of the Catholic threat as Elizabeth I was no longer certain of their loyalty. However, Mary was not executed until 1587.

By 1587, circumstances had changed greatly. England was more under threat from Catholicism than at any time previously. This was reflected in laws and actions against English Catholics becoming much harsher, and Mary's execution in 1587. By 1585, the international context had changed significantly. France and Spain had allied against heresy, and England and Spain were at war. An invasion by 1586 to restore Catholicism and put Mary on the throne was expected as Philip prepared his Armada. Mary's claim to the throne was the same, but the changing international context made it look like it could now succeed. Catholics in England were more suspect than ever. Therefore, Mary, Queen of Scots, had to be executed after the Babington Plot. The actual plot was no more serious than any other, and got no further.

1. a Highlight ✎ where the focus of the question is directly referred to.

   b Underline Ⓐ any mention of when the context of the Catholic threat in England changed.

   c Circle Ⓐ any explanation of how context changed.

   d Draw ✎ an asterisk (*) where the importance of context is identified.

   e Write ✎ a sentence to end the second paragraph more effectively.

....

....

Your turn!

'The main reason the Catholic threat increased in England during 1566–87 was because of the Netherlands.'

How far do you agree? Explain your answer.

You may use the following in your answer:

- the Revolt of the Northern Earls
- Philip II.

You **must** also use information of your own.

(16 marks)

① Write ✎ a paragraph on one aspect of the changing domestic context that caused an increase in the Catholic threat. Focus on explaining why the Duke of Norfolk was not executed in 1569 for his part in the Revolt of the Northern Earls, but was executed for the much less serious Ridolfi Plot, which never got beyond the planning stage.

You should:

- answer the question directly (why was Norfolk executed after the Ridolfi Plot, not before?)
- explain when and how the context of the Catholic threat changed between the Ridolfi Plot and the Revolt of the Northern Earls
- explain how important context is in explaining the different outcome for Norfolk after the Ridolfi Plot.

Here are a few reminders about the Revolt of the Northern Earls to help you choose your paragraph focus:

- **When?** 1569–70
- **Who?** The earls of Northumberland and Westmorland; the Duke of Norfolk; Mary, Queen of Scots
- **What?** Free Mary, Queen of Scots; marry her to Norfolk; overthrow Elizabeth with the help of Spanish troops; put Mary on the throne
- **Scale?** Thousands of Catholic rebels took hold of much of the north of England, including Durham and Hartlepool; Elizabeth I had to raise an army to march north; 450 rebels were executed.

....

....

....

....

....

....

....

....

....

....

....

....

....

....

Review your skills

Check up

Review your response to the exam-style question on page 39. Tick ✓ the column to show how well you think you have done each of the following.

	Had a go ✓	Nearly there ✓	Got it! ✓
identified the key features of the context	☐	☐	☐
showed the influence of context	☐	☐	☐
evaluated the importance of context	☐	☐	☐
maintained focus on the question	☐	☐	☐

Look over all of your work in this unit. Note down ✏ three things you have learned that you will apply when evaluating cause in context.

① ....

② ....

③ ....

Need more practice?

On separate paper, plan and write ✏ your response to the exam-style question below.

Exam-style question

'The actions of Sir Francis Drake were the most important reason for the deterioration in Anglo-Spanish relations in the years 1580–88.'

How far do you agree? Explain your answer.

You may use the following in your answer:

- the singeing of the King of Spain's beard
- the Netherlands.

You **must** also use information of your own.

(16 marks)

How confident do you feel about each of these **skills**? Colour ✏ in the bars.

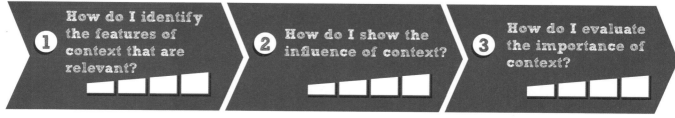

① How do I identify the features of context that are relevant?

② How do I show the influence of context?

③ How do I evaluate the importance of context?

⑤ Evaluating significance

This unit will help you to develop the skills to evaluate significance effectively. The skills you will build are how to:

- assess significance
- show that significance can change
- decide what is most significant.

In the exam, you will be asked to tackle questions such as the one below. This unit will prepare you to write your own response to this type of question.

Exam-style question

> 'The most significant problem facing the Virginia colonies was chance events.'
>
> How far do you agree? Explain your answer.
>
> You may use the following in your answer:
>
> - Chief Wingina
> - the running aground of the *Tiger.*
>
> You **must** also use information of your own.
>
> (16 marks)

There are several things that can help you decide if something is significant, including:

? **frequency** – how often it happened; are there lots of examples of it?

? **quantity** – how many people it affected; how widespread it was, socially and geographically

? **quality** – how deeply it was felt by people

? **longevity** – how long it lasted

It is very important to deal with the stated feature, consequence, factor or problem first when answering an essay question, even if you do not think it is the most significant. In the question above, 'chance events' is the stated problem for you to evaluate.

It is also important to consider relative significance, comparing the significance of different problems, features, causes or consequences. Here are some useful words and phrases you can use to do this:

Although X was significant, Y was more so because …

By 15nn, X was becoming more significant than Y because …

Although X was more important than Y in such and such a place because …

The most significant problem/factor/consequence overall was …

The three key questions in the skills boosts will help you understand how to evaluate significance.

① **How do I assess significance?**

② **How do I show that significance can change?**

③ **How do I decide what is most significant?**

A student studying the question on page 41 collected the following pieces of evidence:

A All supplies on the *Tiger* were ruined when it capsized.

B Colonists set off too late to plant crops for winter.

C Mix of colonists wrong: too many gentry, not enough farmers.

D Harsh climate for settlers – hot, humid in summer; freezing in winter.

E Colonists increasingly demanded help from Native Americans.

F The colonists did not work together.

G Friendly at first, Wingina got other chiefs to join an attack on the English in spring 1586.

H Many colonists had wanted to become rich quickly and were disillusioned.

I Wingina believed the English were supernatural (many locals died from new diseases).

J Wingina was unpredictable and suspicious.

The student then wrote the following conclusion:

Wingina was unpredictable, helping the settlers at first but then changing his mind. In spring 1586, he joined with other Native American tribes to attack the English. It was only because the settlers found out and were prepared that the attack didn't work. Although Wingina was killed, the damage he caused was already done. The surviving colonists left in summer 1586. Wingina was the most significant reason behind the colony's failure.

(1) Look at the evidence in the student's list and sort 🖉 it into the three columns in the table below.

Wingina as a cause	The colonists as a cause	Chance events as a cause

(2) Which column in (1) has the most evidence? How far do you agree that this was the main reason for the failure of the colony? 🖉

....

....

(3) The student looked again at the evidence in the list that suggested the colonists as a cause. She found one piece with a strong link to Wingina. Which piece? 🖉 ....

(4) Look at your answer to (3). Which other pieces of evidence from the list can be linked to it? 🖉

....

(5) Now you have considered the evidence in more detail, look back at your answer to question (2). Draw 🖉 an arrow on the value continuum below to show your answer. Have you changed your mind? Explain 🖉 your decision.

Very little   Partly   Largely   Strongly

....

....

Raleigh and Virginia

This unit uses the theme of Raleigh and Virginia to build your skills in evaluating significance. If you need to review your knowledge of this theme, work through these pages.

1 Draw 🖉 lines linking the answers to the questions.

answer

A Manteo

B Algonquin

C Croatoan

D Grenville

E Raleigh

question

a What was the name of the Native American tribe that inhabited the region of Virginia where the colonies were established?

b Who planned the colonial expeditions and raised the necessary investment?

c Which experienced sailor and soldier led the first colonial expedition in 1585?

d Who came to England in 1584 and returned to Virginia as Lord of Roanoke in 1587?

e What was the name of the friendly Native American tribe attacked by mistake in 1587?

2 Circle Ⓐ the correct answers to the questions below.

a Which of the following was **not** a problem faced by the first colony?

A Their settlement burned down

B Insufficient food over winter

C Left England too late

D Spoiled gunpowder

b Which of the following Native Americans accompanied the colonists?

A Wanchese

B Manteo

C Wingina

D Alsoomse

c Which of the following were the second colonists promised?

A A four-room house

B Two cows and a horse

C 500 acres of land

D £20 if they stayed three years

d Which of these men went on both colonial expeditions?

A Thomas Harriot

B John White

C Thomas Harvey

D Ralph Lane

(3) Tick ✓ whether the following statements are true or false.

	true	false
a Raleigh led the expeditions to colonise Virginia.	☐	☐
b The colonists worked well together to build a strong, stone fort at Roanoke.	☐	☐
c The colonists arrived too late to plant crops for the winter.	☐	☐
d The colonists did not have enough supplies or seeds to plant to survive the winter.	☐	☐
e Manteo and Wanchese led the Native Americans of Roanoke.	☐	☐
f The Native Americans where the colonists settled were Algonquins.	☐	☐
g The colonists were willing to live and work among the Algonquins.	☐	☐

(4) Name 🖊 one way in which the second group of colonists who attempted to settle in Virginia were different from the first.

....

....

....

....

....

(5) Number 🖊 the following events 1–12 to show the order in which they happened.

A Raleigh made Manteo leader of the Virginia colony and John White expedition leader. ☐	B The colonists made more and more demands on the Algonquian. ☐	C Manteo and the colonists attacked friendly Croatoan people by mistake. ☐
D All supplies on the *Tiger* were ruined and the colonists arrived too late to plant anything. ☐	E Five ships left England for Virginia. ☐	F Thomas Harriot wrote an Algonquin–English dictionary. ☐
G Ralph Lane led the surviving colonists back to England. ☐	H A second group of colonists left for Virginia. ☐	I George Howe was murdered by Roanoke people. ☐
J Manteo and Wanchese arrived in England. ☐	K White left for England. When he returned to Virginia, the colonists had disappeared. ☐	L Wingina asked other chiefs to help him attack the colonists. ☐

How do I assess significance?

'How far' questions require you to judge what was the most important (significant) problem, feature, change, cause or consequence. Having more pieces of evidence to support it doesn't necessarily make something the most significant. This skills boost will help you to assess significance. (For more on judgements, see Unit 7.)

A student trying to establish the most significant problem facing the first Virginia colony collected the following evidence:

A All supplies on the *Tiger* were ruined when it capsized.

B The colonists set off too late to plant crops for winter.

C The mix of colonists was wrong: too many gentry, not enough farmers.

D Lane and Grenville, leaders of the 1585 colony, did not get on and divided colonists' loyalties.

E Colonists increasingly demanded help from Native Americans.

F Native Americans thought the colonists were supernatural as they could kill without touching (i.e. the colonists brought new, unknown diseases).

G Wingina was increasingly hostile to the settlers as they demanded more help.

H Wingina was planning to ambush the settlers, so the settlers attacked the Native Americans.

① **a** In the table, write ✏ the letter of each piece of evidence, from the student's list above, that goes with chance events and poor planning. Some pieces of evidence might belong in more than one column.

Factor	Chance events	Poor planning		
Evidence				

b Look at the evidence you have left. What two headings could you group them under? Write ✏ them in the remaining column headings then list the evidence that goes with each underneath.

② One way to assess significance is to look at the quantity of evidence. Given that, which factor do you think was most significant? ✏ ....

Another way to decide if something was significant is to consider how things would have been different without it.

③ Could the first colony have survived if D, E or H hadn't happened? Complete ✓ the table, then pick one and explain your choice. ✏ ....

	Yes, probably ✓	Maybe ✓	No way ✓
D			
E			
H			

....

....

④ If you could pick just one problem from the list without which the 1585 colony would have survived, which would it be and why? ✏

....

⑤ **a** Has your answer to ② changed? ✏ ....

b Which is the more effective way to test signficance: by considering quantity or how things would have been without it? ✏ ....

How do I show that significance can change?

What is significant can vary, with time and place, for example. It can also vary with question focus. This skills boost will help you to compare significance.

A student working on the question of which problems were most significant for the colonies researched the following evidence about the second colony, which had mysteriously disappeared by 1590.

- *Led by Manteo (Lord of Roanoke) and John White (overall; experienced – survived 1585–86)*
- *New colonists from poor parts of London; women and families; promise of a better life*
- *Native Americans hostile from start, e.g. killed White's adviser, leading Manteo to retaliate*
- *Manteo attacked friendly Croatoan people by mistake*

(1) Look at the table below. In order to show that significance can change, compare the problems across the first and second colonies by placing a tick ⊘ if those of the first colony also affected the second.

Problems faced by the first colony (1585)	Problems faced by the second colony (1587) ⊘
Poor planning – wrong mix of colonists, arrived too late to plant crops	
Bad luck	
First attempt, so colonists were inexperienced	
Wingina	
Violent clashes between Native Americans and settlers	
Poor leadership – for example, Grenville and Lane did not get on	

(2) What was the most significant problem for each colony? Explain ✎ your choice.

a *The most significant problem of the first colony was:* ....

because ....

b *The most significant problem of the second colony was:* ....

because ....

(3) Write ✎ a conclusion of 2–3 sentences to explain whether chance events were always the most significant problem facing the Virginia colonies. You should show that significance can change.

....

....

....

....

....

....

3 How do I decide what is most significant?

Sometimes the question suggests what is most significant. Be prepared to challenge the question. This skills boost will help you to decide what is most significant.

Raleigh: expedition organiser	Chief Wingina
Actions: raised finance, organised ships and supplies and recruited colonists. He was not allowed to go on the expedition himself.	**Actions:** friendly at first, but he refused to help the colonists survive the winter. In spring 1586, he planned to attack them.

① The table above shows details of both Raleigh and Wingina. In order to compare significance, look at the

actions of each. Who do you think was more to blame for the failure of the colony? ....

One way of deciding the significance of a cause, consequence or change is to look at its interaction with other causes, consequences or changes. Study these four reasons in one student's notes for the failure of the 1585 colony:

A _Chief Wingina_ How helpful was he? An unpredictable man, his patience with the colonists' demands for help soon ran out. In spring 1586, he planned an attack on the colonists.

B _The colonists_ How fit for purpose were they? They expected to rule the Algonquins and get rich quickly. Many were gentry, not used to work. They relied on handouts from the Algonquins.

C _The planning of the expedition_ How good was it? Raleigh raised the finance, organised ships and supplies; and chose the colonists. The expedition left too late to plant crops for winter.

D _Chance events_ How unlucky were they? The Tiger ran aground. It carried most of the vital supplies, which spoiled. The colonists brought diseases that killed the local people, who thought they were magic.

② **a** Consider which was the most significant reason (A–D) for the failure of the 1585 colony by looking at the impact of each on the others. Did A (Wingina) have a knock-on effect on B? C? D? Briefly explain any knock-on effects below. If there are none, leave the answer line blank. One has been done to help you.

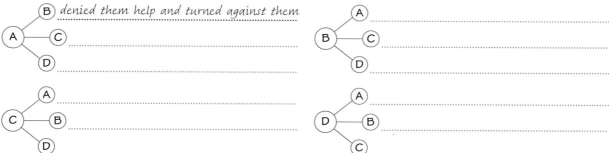

b Look at your answers for ② **a** . Which reason(s) are most important (interact(s) most with other reasons)?

....

....

> **Remember:**
> - Significance is not necessarily based on how much evidence there is.
> - What is significant can change with time and context.
> - What is significant can be determined by its impact on or interaction with other developments.

Sample response

'The colonists themselves were to blame for the failure of the Virginia colonies in the years 1585–87.'

How far do you agree? Explain your answer.

Here are three students' responses to the exam-style question above.

Answer A

The colonists were significantly to blame for the failure of both colonies. If they had been able to work with the Algonquins better, they could have survived. Wingina was significant because he refused to help them, so could be significant too. The second lot of colonists disappeared. When White returned to Virginia in 1590, he found only the word 'Croatoan' carved on a post. This could mean that the Croatoans killed them. The colonists, led by Manteo, had killed friendly Croatoans just before White left for England.

Answer B

The colonists were to blame for the failure of both colonies. The first colonists demanded too much from the Algonquins and Wingina, their unpredictable chief, soon tired of demands for handouts of his people's food. He turned against the colonists, many of whom did not survive the winter without the help they needed. If the expedition had been properly planned, it might have left in time to plant crops; and if the supplies had been shared between different ships for the dangerous voyage, it would not have mattered so much when the Tiger ran aground. So, poor planning was to blame for the failure of the colonies. The problems it caused in 1585 led the Native Americans to begin to be hostile to the colonists in 1586 and 1587.

Answer C

Poor planning, rather than the colonists themselves, was certainly the most significant cause of the failure of the first colony. By causing hostility between the colonists and the Native Americans, it contributed greatly to the failure of the second. Although the second colonists were better prepared, they faced hostility from the Algonquins. They made Native American hostility worse when they killed friendly Croatoans by mistake. Nevertheless, had the first expedition set off in time to plant crops, and had it not lost the bulk of its supplies when the Tiger ran aground, the 1585 colonists would have been less reliant on Wingina and could have formed better relationships with them. Another reason why poor planning led to hostility was that the 1585 colonists were not suitable. Many wanted to get rich quickly and expected to rule the Native Americans, who they thought would do the work. So, although Native American hostility was more significant from the very start of the 1587 colony, the problems caused by poor planning in 1585 can be said to have been most significant overall.

(1) Read the students' responses and complete ✓ the table to highlight the strengths of each.

Has the answer ...	A ✓	B ✓	C ✓
clearly highlighted the most significant cause?			
supported it with specific evidence?			
shown how it impacted on other factors?			
shown any change of significant factor over time?			

Your turn!

'Wingina was the most significant reason for the failure of the Virginia colonies.'

How far do you agree? Explain your answer.

You may use the following in your answer:

- Walter Raleigh
- inexperience.

You **must** also use information of your own.

(16 marks)

(1) Draw up ✐ a plan for an answer to the question above.

(2) Write ✐ the introduction and conclusion to go with your plan. The introduction must be clear about how far you think Wingina was the most significant reason for the failure of the Virginia colonies, and also identify other reasons and how important they were. Your conclusion must summarise the main points of your plan and show how far you agree with the statement in the question.

Review your skills

Check up

Review your response to the exam-style question on page 49. Tick ✓ the column to show how well you think you have done each of the following.

	Had a go ✓	Nearly there ✓	Got it! ✓
identified what was significant	☐	☐	☐
showed how significance changed over time	☐	☐	☐
showed what was most significant	☐	☐	☐
supported my points with evidence	☐	☐	☐

Look over all of your work in this unit. Note down ✐ three things you have learned that you will apply when evaluating significance.

① ....

② ....

③ ....

Need more practice?

On separate paper, plan and write ✐ your response to the exam-style question below.

Exam-style question

'The Puritans posed the most significant threat to the Elizabethan religious settlement 1558–69.'

How far do you agree? Explain your answer.

You may use the following in your answer:

• the vestments controversy
• the oath of supremacy.

You must also use information of your own.

(16 marks)

How confident do you feel about each of these **skills**? Colour in ✐ the bars.

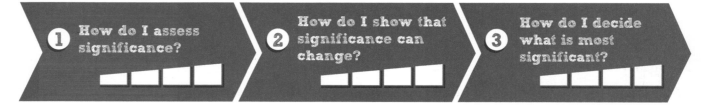

① How do I assess significance?

② How do I show that significance can change?

③ How do I decide what is most significant?

⑥ Evaluating consequence

Students answering questions involving consequence often wander off focus. Essays on consequence must analyse results or effects and their impact, ensuring their relevance to the points in the question. This unit will help you to develop the skills to evaluate consequence effectively. The skills you will build are how to:

- identify consequences
- show how/why something is a consequence
- decide on the main consequence.

In the exam, you will be asked to tackle questions such as the one below. This unit will prepare you to write your own response to this type of question.

Exam-style question

'The most important consequence of Drake's voyages 1577–87 was that they made Philip II of Spain angry.'

How far do you agree? Explain your answer.

You may use the following in your answer:

- Elizabeth I's knighting of Drake
- Philip II's decision to build the Armada.

You **must** also use information of your own.

(16 marks)

Types of consequence

As well as being political, economic, social or religious, for example, consequences can be immediate, short-term or long-term. Sometimes the most significant consequences are only realised a long time after the events that led to them happened.

Consequences can also be intended or unintended. Intended consequences are anticipated when actions are planned. However, even the best-laid plans can have surprise results. These are unintended consequences.

The three key questions in the **skills boosts** will help you to evaluate consequences.

 1 How do I identify a consequence?

2 How do I show that something is a consequence?

 3 How do I decide on the main consequence?

Here is a student's plan for an answer to the exam-style question on page 51.

<u>Intro</u>

Overview of the aims of Drake's three voyages (circumnavigation, raiding Spanish New World territories, attacking Spanish navy in Cadiz)

<u>Paragraph 1</u>

Circumnavigation 1577–80. Aim = be first English person to sail around world (although there is some doubt about this being his main aim)
Also to make money and raid Spanish colonies
Plus explain why Elizabeth I wanted revenge on Spain – Anglo-Spanish relations deteriorating

<u>Paragraph 2</u>

Nova Albion – what/where was it; coronation ceremony

Drake returned with huge sums of money but only 1 ship and 56 men
Elizabeth I knighted Drake, making Philip II furious

<u>Paragraph 3</u>

1585: Elizabeth I sent Drake to raid Spanish New World colonies to disrupt Philip II's flow of resources
Philip II angered by yet more of Drake's raids on top of others

This voyage probably persuaded Philip II to go ahead with Armada

<u>Paragraph 4</u>

England and Spain at war. Drake's raid was daring. He attacked Spanish navy over 3 days, destroyed 30 ships, known as 'singeing of the King of Spain's beard' – bound to anger Philip II. Plus, Drake went on to the New World.

<u>Conclusion</u>

Yes – Drake's voyages made Philip II angry

---

① **a** Highlight 🖉 the plan where the student has identified consequences of the voyages.

   b Cross out ~~out~~ anything irrelevant to the question.

② Draw 🖉 an arrow on the value continuum below to show how well this plan focuses on consequence.

Throughout (4/4 – all paragraphs)	Strongly (3/4 paragraphs)	Partially (2/4 paragraphs)	Poorly (1/4 paragraphs)	Not at all (0/4 paragraphs)

Exploration and voyages of discovery

This unit uses the theme of exploration and voyages of discovery to help you build your skills in evaluating consequence. If you need to review your knowledge of this theme, work through these pages.

① Draw 🖉 lines linking the explorers, the dates and the voyages of discovery. Use three different styles for the lines; for example, a solid line for Drake, a dashed line for Hawkins and a dotted line for Raleigh.

who	when	significance
Drake	A 1562	a Circumnavigation of the globe
	B 1567–68	b Conflict with Spain at St Juan de Ulúa, Mexico
	C 1571–72	c Elizabeth I invested in this voyage to Panama, which captured £40,000 of Spanish treasure
Hawkins	D 1577–80	d Factfinding mission to Virginia
	E 1584	e First group of colonists sent to Virginia
	F 1585	f First transatlantic triangular trade expedition
Raleigh	G 1587	g Second group of colonists to Virginia

② Circle Ⓐ the correct answers below about Drake's circumnavigation of the globe.

a How many ships did Drake leave with?

A One B Five C Eight D Ten

b What territory did Drake claim for England?

A California B St Juan de Ulúa C Virginia D Nova Albion

c How many ships did Drake return with?

A None B One C Two D Three

d How much treasure did Drake bring back?

A £400,000 B £328,000 C £150,000 D £128,000

e Which of the following were consequences of Drake's circumnavigation?

A Encouraged more exploration of America

B Angered Philip II of Spain

C Important boost to English morale

D Encouraged plans to colonise America

3 The following statements are all inaccurate; for each one, write 🖊 a sentence explaining why.

a | In 1585, Elizabeth I sent Drake to raid Spain's ports in the Netherlands.

....

b | The consequence of Drake's 1585 raids was that the pope told Philip II to invade England.

....

c | In April 1587, Drake sailed into Cadiz harbour and destroyed 19 Spanish ships.

....

d | The raid on Cadiz harbour had little or no impact on the final launch of the Armada.

....

e | After attacking Cadiz, Drake sailed straight for South America to attack Spain's colonies.

....

f | Drake's attack on Cadiz made Elizabeth I much less secure on her throne.

....

4 Write 🖊 numbers 1–4 in the boxes to put the following voyages in chronological order.

A | Colonists set sail on the first attempt to colonise Virginia.

B | Drake returns from his circumnavigation of the globe.

C | New colonists set off for a second attempt to colonise Virginia.

D | Raleigh sends a fact-finding mission to Virginia.

5 Circle Ⓐ which of the following are the odd ones out and explain 🖊 why.

a | The Azores   Mexico   California   Peru

....

....

b | establish an English colony   revenge   profit   raid Spain's New World colonies

....

....

c | *Tiger*   *Golden Hind*   *Lion*   *Elizabeth*   *Dorothy*

....

....

1 How do I identify a consequence?

A consequence is the result of an action or an event. Identifying consequences requires looking at the impact of events. Make sure that in an answer about consequences, your focus stays on consequences. This skills boost will help you to understand how to identify consequences.

It is essential to be able to differentiate between causes and consequences.

1 **a** Tick ✓ which of the following are causes that answer the question: Why did Drake circumnavigate the globe?

b Tick ✓ which of the following are consequences that answer the question: What did Drake's circumnavigation lead to?

		question **a** (why?)	question **b** (consequence)
A	Drake wanted revenge for St Juan de Ulúa.	☐	☐
B	Drake returned with only one ship and 56 men.	☐	☐
C	The circumnavigation led to more exploration.	☐	☐
D	As a result of the circumnavigation, Elizabeth I knighted Drake.	☐	☐
E	The circumnavigation turned out to be a success for Drake's investors.	☐	☐
F	The Native Americans were very hospitable.	☐	☐
G	Drake became the first English sailor to circumnavigate the globe.	☐	☐
H	Drake wanted to be the first English sailor to circumnavigate the globe.	☐	☐
I	Investors in the voyage wanted to become rich.	☐	☐
J	Investors in the voyage became very rich.	☐	☐

An introduction needs to give details of consequences. It should include the one in the question and other significant ones. This is the introduction to a student's answer to the exam-style question on page 51:

> Drake made three important voyages between 1577 and 1587, each of which angered Philip II. Throughout this time, Anglo-Spanish relations were deteriorating, and Drake's voyages contributed to this. Elizabeth I wanted to disrupt Philip II's flows of resources from the New World. This was why Drake's 1585 voyage was so important: because it disrupted Philip II's flows of resources from the New World when England and Spain were at war. Philip II was so angry that this voyage triggered the building of the Armada. The 1587 voyage was even more important as it gave England time to prepare defences against the Armada, which it defeated.

2 **a** Underline Ⓐ where the consequences of Drake's voyages on Philip's anger have been indicated.

b Circle Ⓐ where the student has suggested other consequences of Drake's voyages.

c Refer back to your list in question **1** **b**. What consequences would you expect to find in the essay that are missing from the student's introduction? ✎

....

2 How do I show that something is a consequence?

Something which happens after an event does not automatically make it a consequence of that event. For it to be a consequence, it needs to happen **as a result** of the event, or be **an effect** of it. This skills boost will demonstrate how to show that something is a consequence.

(1) All the events in the list below happened after Drake's circumnavigation voyage began, but which are linked to it? Place a cross ⊗ alongside any that are **not** consequences of Drake's voyages 1577–87.

A | The founding of Nova Albion

B | Only 56 survivors returned from the circumnavigation

C | Raleigh sent a factfinding mission to North America

D | Its success proved English ships and sailors were among the best in the world

E | England and the Netherlands signed the Treaty of Nonsuch

F | Philip II decided to build the Armada

G | The 1585 colony in Virginia

H | Drake returned with wealth and useful reports about North America

Drake's circumnavigation ended in 1580. It was one of many factors that resulted in a colony being established in Virginia in 1585. The colony was **not** a direct consequence, however.

There are immediate consequences and wider ones that stretch into the long term. An event can lead to a lot of different consequences, some of which link together to lead to an outcome much later on — one thing leads to another. These are called **knock-on effects**.

(2) Write down ✏ which **three** events from the list above, in which order, link the circumnavigation with the 1585 colony.

| 1580: Circumnavigation | ⇨ | ⇨ | ⇨ | 1585: Virginia Colony |

Consequences can also be intended (planned) and unintended (unplanned) when an action is taken. They can also be positive or negative.

(3) Look at the consequences of Drake's circumnavigation in the table below. Tick ✓ if they were long- or short-term, intended or unintended consequences.

Consequence	Immediate (short-term) ✓	Long-term ✓	Intended ✓	Unintended ✓
A Only 56 survivors returned				
B English ships and sailors proven among the best in the world				
C Raleigh sent a factfinding mission to Virginia				

3 How do I decide on the main consequence?

Events usually have many different consequences. This skills boost will help you to decide which is the most important.

In order to decide what the main consequences of an event were, you need to consider its long-term consequences. You need to ask 'What did it lead to?'

① Using the letters of the statements below, make a chain of consequences that connects Drake's circumnavigation to the failure of the Virginian colonies.

| Drake's circumnavigation | | | | Failure of the Virginian colonies |

A | Further exploration of North America
D | England seen as a great sea-faring nation

B | Drake being knighted by Elizabeth I
E | The failure of two Virginia colonies

C | England's first attempts to colonise Virginia
F | The worsening of Anglo-Spanish relations

② Of all the consequences A–F above, which do you think was the most important to Elizabethan England, and why?

You might like to consider the following when thinking about the significance of its impact:
- quantity: How many people were affected? How widespread was it, socially and geographically?
- quality: How deeply was it felt by people at the time?

....

....

....

The table below lists the consequences of two of Drake's voyages.

1577 circumnavigation	1586 raids against Spain
A Drake brought back £400,000, making himself and his investors very wealthy	A Humiliation for Philip II
B Boosted English morale and established England as a great sea-faring nation	B Destruction of 30 Spanish ships and supplies, and capture of a Spanish treasure ship
C Encouraged further exploration of America	C The delay of the Armada
D Damaged Anglo-Spanish relations	D Spain was less prepared and England had more time to prepare
E Raleigh established the first Virginia colonies	E The Armada was defeated

③ Put each consequence from the lists above in the appropriate cell in the table below.

Consequence	1577 circumnavigation	1586 raids
Positive		
Negative		
Short-term		
Long-term		

④ Overall, which voyage had the most significant consequences for Elizabethan England? Write your answer on a separate piece of paper.

Sample response

Knowing what a good answer looks like can help you to model your own responses.

'The most important consequence of Drake's voyages 1577–87 was that they made Philip II of Spain angry.'

How far do you agree? Explain your answer.

You may use the following in your answer:

- Elizabeth I's knighting of Drake
- Philip II's decision to build the Armada.

You **must** also use information of your own.

(16 marks)

Read the following student's answer to the exam-style question above.

Drake's voyages had the very important consequences for his investors of making huge profits. For example, in 1572 he returned with £40,000 from Panama, and in 1580 he returned with £400,000 – ten times that. This prompted further exploration of North America.

Another reason why voyages of exploration to the New World were undertaken was that adventure was important to Elizabethan gentlemen. More important, however, was to raid Spain's New World colonies and disrupt Philip II's flow of wealth and resources. Elizabeth I made this clear to Drake in her secret orders before he set off for his circumnavigation. In fact, Drake's circumnavigation is often said to be an unintended consequence of what was supposed to be another privateering expedition against the Spanish.

Although Philip II was angered by Elizabeth I's knighting of Drake in 1580, the decision to build an Armada was the consequence of Drake's 1585 raids on Spanish New World colonies. By this time the international context had changed. England and Spain were at war, which made Philip II's anger as a result of this latest raid a far more significant consequence than it had been in 1580. Drake's raids, ordered by Elizabeth I, had now resulted in seriously endangering England.

It was another consequence of one of Drake's raids, however, that lessened the danger. This was in April 1587. The ultimate outcome was the defeat of the Armada.

(1) Look for the following strengths:

a Draw (✏) an asterisk (*) where the stated consequence in the question has been directly addressed.

b Circle (Ⓐ) where consequences other than the one stated in the question are identified.

c Underline (Ⓐ) where the type of consequence is referenced (e.g. intended/unintended).

d Double underline (Ⓐ) where the importance of the consequences is mentioned.

Your turn!

Now it's your turn to try to answer an exam-style question.

Exam-style question

'The most important consequence of Drake's voyages during 1577–87 was that they made Philip II of Spain angry.'

How far do you agree? Explain your answer.

You may use the following in your answer:

- Elizabeth I's knighting of Drake
- Philip II's decision to build the Armada.

You **must** also use information of your own.

(16 marks)

1. Write ✏ two paragraphs in the space below focusing on the consequences of Drake's voyages during 1577–87. Identify the types of consequences you write about. Here is a list of different types of consequences for you to think about:

| Immediate | Long-term | Knock-on | Unintended | Positive | Negative |

2. At the end of the second paragraph, using terms from the list in 1 to justify your argument, say whether you think the most important consequence of Drake's voyages 1577–87 was that they made Philip II of Spain angry. ✏

....
....
....
....
....
....
....
....
....
....
....
....
....
....
....
....
....

Review your skills

Check up

Review your response to the exam-style question on page 59. Tick ✓ the column to show how well you think you have done each of the following.

	Had a go ✓	Nearly there ✓	Got it! ✓
clearly identified key consequences	☐	☐	☐
focused on consequences	☐	☐	☐
made judgements about how significant the consequences were	☐	☐	☐
supported judgements about consequences	☐	☐	☐

Look over all of your work in this unit. Note down ✐ three things you have learned that you will apply when evaluating consequence.

① ....

② ....

③ ....

Need more practice?

On separate paper, plan and write ✐ your response to the exam-style question below.

> **Exam-style question**
>
> 'The most significant consequence of changes in education in Elizabethan England was the increase in literacy.'
>
> How far do you agree? Explain your answer.
>
> You may use the following in your answer:
>
> • universities
> • girls' education.
>
> You **must** also use information of your own.
>
> (16 marks)

How confident do you feel about each of these **skills**? Colour ✐ in the bars.

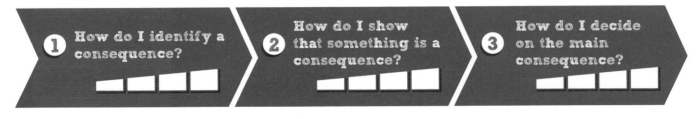

1 How do I identify a consequence?

2 How do I show that something is a consequence?

3 How do I decide on the main consequence?

7 Making judgements

There is no such thing as a 'right' judgement; there is such a thing as a 'good' or convincing judgement. There is a challenge in doing this: you cannot ignore important evidence because it doesn't fit your answer! This unit will help you to develop the skills to make judgements effectively. The skills you will build are how to:

* organise information to make a judgement
* deal with conflicting evidence
* make a convincing judgement.

In the exam, you will be asked to tackle questions such as the one below. This unit will prepare you to write your own response to this type of question.

Exam-style question

'The problem of the succession was the most important reason for the Revolt of the Northern Earls of 1569–70.'

How far do you agree? Explain your answer.

You may use the following in your answer:

* the Duke of Norfolk
* Roman Catholicism.

You **must** also use information of your own.

(16 marks)

The signs of strong judgements in an essay include:

* the judgement is in the introduction and can be followed through to the conclusion
* the relative importance of the stated factor compared with other factors is considered
* evidence that doesn't fit the judgement is dealt with
* the focus on the question is maintained and the answer links back to it throughout.

Here are some more points to remember about making judgements:

* For 'how far do you agree' questions, your judgement will be how far you agree!
* Judgements on historical questions are unlikely to be 100% agreement or disagreement; be prepared to challenge the statement!

You will need to apply your skills from Unit 5, on evaluating significance, to help you reach your judgements.

The three key questions in the **skills boosts** will help you to answer judgement questions effectively.

 1 How do I use my information to make a judgement?

 2 How do I deal with conflicting evidence?

3 How do I ensure I make a convincing judgement?

A student planning an answer to the exam-style question on page 61 gathered the following evidence.

1 Aim = marry Mary to Norfolk, (who said he was Protestant) for heirs

2 Many Catholics did not accept Elizabeth's legitimacy

3 The north of England was largely Catholic

4 The rebels held Catholic mass in Durham

5 There was the rise of new, lower class Protestants at court e.g. Cecil, Leicester.

6 The northern earls were Catholic but Elizabeth I was Protestant

7 The northern earls, from old noble families, had lost influence at court to the newcomers

First, he counted how many pieces of evidence supported the idea that the succession was the most important reason for causing the Revolt of the Northern Earls of 1569.

(1) (a) How many pieces of evidence suggest that the succession was a cause of the Revolt of the Northern Earls of 1569? Note (✎) your answer in the second column of the table.

Possible reasons for opposition to the religious settlement	How many pieces of evidence?	How important? (Very, quite or not very important)
A The succession		
B Religion		
C Court politics		
D The overthrow of Elizabeth I		

(b) Based on that, how important was the succession as a reason for the Revolt of the Northern Earls? Use the scale below and note (✎) your answer in the third column of the table above.

Very important (5+ pieces of evidence)	Quite important (3–4 pieces of evidence)	Not very important (1–2 pieces of evidence)

(c) Repeat (1) (a) and (b) for each of the other possible reasons for the Revolt of the Northern Earls listed and complete (✎) the table.

(2) Review your answers to question (1). According to the quantities of evidence, which was/were the most important reason(s) for the Revolt of the Northern Earls? (✎)

....

....

(3) What drawbacks are there in using this method (counting up the pieces of evidence) to come to a judgement? (✎)

....

....

....

The Revolt of the Northern Earls

This unit uses the theme of the Revolt of the Northern Earls, 1569–70, to build your skills in making judgements. If you need to review your knowledge of this theme, work through these pages.

1 **a** Circle Ⓐ which of the following were involved in plotting the Revolt of the Northern Earls.

A | Earl of Cumberland

B | Earl of Westmorland

C | Earl of Northumberland

D | Duke of Suffolk

E | Duke of Norfolk

b Circle Ⓐ which of the following were resented, or disliked by those behind the rebellion.

A | John Forster

B | John Fortescue

C | William Cecil

D | Robert Dudley

E | James Pilkington

c Circle Ⓐ who alerted Elizabeth I to the 1569 plot.

A | William Cecil

B | Robert Dudley

C | Francis Walsingham

D | John Fortescue

d Circle Ⓐ who the focus of the plot was.

A | Mary, Queen of Scots, and Norfolk

B | Mary, Queen of Scots, and Suffolk

C | Mary, Queen of Scots, and Northumberland

D | Mary, Queen of Scots, and Westmorland

2 Tick ✓ whether the following statements are true or false.

		true	false
a	Jane Neville and Ann Percy were against the revolt.		
b	Elizabeth I was undecided about whether to marry Eric of Sweden or the Duke of Alençon.		
c	The revolt began as a court conspiracy involving Robert Dudley.		
d	The rebels hoped that French troops would arrive in Hartlepool to support them.		
e	It was planned that the Duke of Norfolk should march to London to overthrow Elizabeth I.		
f	Elizabeth I offered to release Mary, Queen of Scots, from captivity if the revolt was ended.		

3 Who was the newly appointed Bishop of Durham? ✎

....

....

4 Circle (A) the odd ones out. Explain (✏) your choice.

a | Durham | Hartlepool | London | York |

....

b | Earl of Huntingdon | Earl of Westmorland | Earl of Northumberland | Earl of Leicester |

....

c | copper mine | England's northern border | the succession | Duke of Alençon |

....

5 The following statements all contain mistakes. Write (✏) your correction below each one.

a | The papal bull excommunicating Elizabeth I was an important reason for the rebellion. |

....

....

b | The Earl of Westmorland was captured and executed. |

....

....

c | After the rebellion, 4,500 rebels were executed across northern England. |

....

....

d | Elizabeth I sent someone more sympathetic to Catholics to govern northern England. |

....

....

6 Write (✏) the numbers 1–7 in the boxes to put the events in the correct chronological order.

A | Some rebels diverted to Hartlepool hoping to meet up with Spanish support | ☐

B | All of northern England east of the Pennines and south of Braham Moor held by rebels | ☐

C | Earl of Sussex began raising troops in the North to put down the revolt | ☐

D | Royal forces crossed the River Tees | ☐

E | Bells were rung at Topcliffe | ☐

F | The rebel earls crossed into Scotland | ☐

G | Durham Cathedral was seized and a Catholic mass held | ☐

1 How do I use my information to make a judgement?

When using the information you have to make a judgement, do not simply look at the quantity of evidence you have for any one cause, consequence or change. This skills boost will help you to consider the impact of evidence you have on the outcome you are studying.

① Use the evidence from page 62 to complete the table below.

Evidence suggesting the succession was important	Evidence linking the succession to other causes	Evidence suggesting the succession was not important

Don't just look at the **quantity** of evidence. Think about how different events and circumstances would **contribute** to the outcome. Some would play a very important role, others a lesser one.

② Taking all the evidence into consideration, mark on the continuum below what you think about whether the succession was the most important reason for the Revolt of the Northern Earls. Briefly explain your choice below.

Disagree 100%	Disagree strongly	Disagree more than agree	Agree more than disagree	Agree strongly	Agree 100%

....

③ The student from page 62 decided religion was the most important reason for the Revolt of the Northern Earls. Which of these plans is better for answering the question? Explain your choice using the guidelines given in the Introduction to this unit.

> Use your skills on evaluation of significance from Unit 5 to help you make your judgement.

Plan A

1 Explain why religion was the most important reason for the rebellion.
2 Explain why Mary, Queen of Scots, was the next most important; include links to religion.
3 Explain why court politics was the next most important reason, including links to religion.
4 Explain why I disagree that succession was very important. Include links back to religion.
5 Conclusion: recap why religion was more important than succession.

Plan B

1 Explain how succession was important but not the **most** important reason.
2 Explain why religion was an important reason; explain any links to succession.
3 Explain why Mary was important; including links to succession.
4 Explain why politics was a less important reason; explain any links to succession.
5 Conclusion: recap key points why succession **not** most important but religion is.

....

....

How do I deal with conflicting evidence?

Knowing how to deal with conflicting evidence is very important in making effective judgements. This skills boost will help you understand how to deal with conflicting evidence.

So, was the succession the most important reason for the Revolt of the Northern Earls?

A Yes, the succession was the most important reason. The rebellion began as a plot to provide England with an heir. Marrying Mary, Queen of Scots, to Norfolk remained a key aim of the plot.

B Religion was the most important cause. A Catholic monarch would end *all* the earls' concerns, political ones too. The succession was the aim when courtiers like Leicester were involved.

C The aim changed to replacing Elizabeth I with Mary, Queen of Scots. The idea was that she would marry Norfolk who, as her husband, could take control. This would get rid of men like Cecil and Leicester too. It was about a complete change of government – politics was the most important reason.

D Court politics did not concern the ordinary rebels. The succession wasn't important to them like religion was. They carried religious banners and heard Mass in Durham. They hated the Protestant religious settlement and wanted to restore Catholicism as the main religion in England.

Conflicting evidence can help to establish a debate in your answer, either by looking more carefully at why it conflicts, or by acknowledging the differences. You could use the following phrases in your answer.

> **Why is there conflicting evidence? Because it can vary according to when, who, where**
>
> - While X was more important when …, Y became more important when … (time frame)
> - Although X was more important to …, Y was more important to … (different people/groups)
> - Although X was more important where …, Y was more important where … (geography)
>
> **Acknowledge the differences**
>
> - It is true that X was at least partly a reason for … However, Y cannot be ignored because …
> - Although X was certainly a factor in …, Y was perhaps more important because …
> - From one point of view, X can be seen as more important because …, but from another, Y is …

Read the statements A–D.

1 **a** Why is there conflict between A and C? 🖉

....

b Why is there conflict between B and D? 🖉

....

2 Using the phrases in the box, write 🖉 a sentence combining the conflicting evidence in

a C and D. ....

....

b A and B. ....

....

3 How do I ensure I make a convincing judgement?

A convincing judgement is the one you most believe in after weighing the evidence and taking other options into account. This skills boost will help you to make a convincing judgement.

A student made the following notes for an answer to this question:

Exam-style question

'Court politics was the most important reason for the Revolt of the Northern Earls.'

How far do you agree? Explain your answer.

A convincing judgement will:
• focus on the question – use the key words from the question to start your judgement
• weigh up *all* the evidence – acknowledge that there are alternative points of view
• support your judgement – identify and explain the key evidence that led to your judgement.

> Northern earls were from ancient Catholic nobility, had lost influence at court
> under Elizabeth I to new, Protestant men, e.g. Cecil, Leicester. Political rivalry =
> important and partly based on religion.
>
> Plot began with aim of securing an heir for Elizabeth I by marrying Mary, Queen
> of Scots, to Norfolk, but developed into replacing Elizabeth I with Catholic Mary.
> Succession was not very important. Shows the plot was political, but also religious as it
> was about having a Catholic monarch.
>
> Ordinary rebels in north focused on restoring Catholicism (religious banners, Mass
> at Durham).

To answer the exam-style question at the top of the page, one student's judgement using the notes above was that it was largely court politics that led to the Revolt of the Northern Earls.

① Underline Ⓐ the evidence in the student's notes above that best supports their judgement. Look back at page 65 if you need some help.

Two students' judgements were that it was religion that led to the Revolt of the Northern Earls. One gave the aim to put a Catholic queen on the throne as the strongest evidence for this; the other quoted thousands of ordinary rebels aiming to restore Catholicism.

② Which student's choice of supporting evidence makes a stronger, more convincing point? Explain your choice, remembering to weigh the evidence and consider all options. Your choice will be the one that you believe in and can explain persuasively. ✎

....

....

....

....

Remember: The question is **how far** court politics was the most important reason for the Revolt of the Northern Earls.

Sample response

Making effective judgements is an important skill. Knowing the difference between a convincing and an unconvincing judgement will help you to model your own.

> ### Exam-style question
>
> 'Mary, Queen of Scots' claim to the throne was the most important reason for the Revolt of the Northern Earls.'
>
> How far do you agree? Explain your answer.

In response to the exam-style question above, a student wrote the judgement below.

Religion was very important for the ordinary rebels. The North was very Catholic, and resented the new Protestant Bishop of Durham. This was made clear by holding Mass in Durham cathedral. However, it was court politics and a loss of status that drove the leaders of the rebellion, making it more important than religion because without leadership the discontent of the ordinary people would not have led to rebellion. The plot started with the aim of marrying Mary, Queen of Scots, to the Duke of Norfolk in order to secure the succession, as she had the best claim to the throne. It quickly developed into something much more important: a plot to overthrow Elizabeth I. The earls greatly resented newcomers like Cecil and Leicester, who were Protestants like Elizabeth I. Overthrowing Elizabeth I's government and replacing her with the Catholic Mary would solve all the rebels' problems: the Catholic earls would regain their political status and Catholicism would be restored. Religion was not the main reason for the rebellion, although it was important. Ultimately, however, the Revolt of the Northern Earls was about regime change stemming from court politics.

The judgement shows the following strengths:

- It deals with the stated factor, despite not believing it was the most important cause. This means it has directly addressed the question.
- It gives a clear judgement about what the most important cause is.
- It shows the relative importance of the key causes compared with its most important cause. This means it has not ignored the evidence that doesn't fit with its judgement.
- It provides support for its judgement. This means that it shows the reasoning behind the judgement.

(1) **a** Highlight (✐) where a judgement on the importance of the stated factor (Mary, Queen of Scots' claim to the throne) as a cause has been made.

b Underline (Ⓐ) where a judgement about the most important cause has been made.

c Circle (Ⓐ) any evidence or reasons put forward to support court politics as the most important cause of the Revolt of the Northern Earls.

d Draw an asterisk (*) (✐) where words and phrases have addressed conflicting evidence.

e Pick one sentence you think best presents the student's point of view and double underline (Ⓐ) it. Look for a clearly explained, well-supported point made on their view about the reason for the Revolt of the Northern Earls.

Your turn!

Now it's your turn to try to answer an exam-style question.

Exam-style question

'Religion was the most important reason for the Revolt of the Northern Earls.'

How far do you agree? Explain your answer.

You may use the following in your answer:

- the Earl of Northumberland
- the problem of the succession.

You **must** also use information of your own.

(16 marks)

(1) What evidence is there that religion was the most important reason for the Revolt of the Northern Earls? On a separate piece of paper, draw up this table to help you decide.

Evidence yes	Evidence no

(2) From your 'Evidence no' column, what reasons other than religion are there?

....

....

(3) Write 2–3 sentences supporting the view in the question.

....

....

(4) Write 2–3 sentences supporting another reason (your choice) for the Revolt of the Northern Earls.

....

....

(5) Bring your answers to (3) and (4) together in a short paragraph that explains which reason is the most important and to what extent. It should also include the other, conflicting point of view – to what extent was it important in comparison?

....

....

....

....

....

....

....

....

Review your skills

Check up

Review your response to the exam-style question on page 69. Tick ✓ the column to show how well you think you have done each of the following.

	Had a go ✓	Nearly there ✓	Got it! ✓
used my information to develop an effective judgement	☐	☐	☐
considered deciding factors to assess how far I agree with the statement	☐	☐	☐
looked at the stated feature in comparison with other causes	☐	☐	☐
dealt with conflicting evidence in making my judgement	☐	☐	☐

Look over all of your work in this unit. Note down ✎ three things you have learned that you will apply when making judgements.

① ....

② ....

③ ....

Need more practice?

On separate paper, plan and write ✎ your response to the exam-style question below.

Exam-style question

'Colonisation was the most important consequence of the voyages of Sir Francis Drake in the years 1568–87.'

How far do you agree? Explain your answer.

You may use the following in your answer:

- the Virginia colonies
- circumnavigation.

You **must** also use information of your own.

(16 marks)

How confident do you feel about each of these **skills**? Colour ✎ in the bars.

① How do I use my information to make a judgement? ☐☐☐☐

② How do I deal with conflicting evidence? ☐☐☐☐

③ How do I ensure I make a convincing judgement? ☐☐☐☐

Get started

⑧ Writing effective conclusions

This unit will help you to develop the skills to write conclusions effectively. The skills you will build are how to:

- recognise the features of a successful conclusion
- show in the conclusion why one element is more important than others
- construct an effective conclusion.

In the exam, you will be asked to tackle questions such as the one below. This unit will prepare you to write your own response to this type of question.

Exam-style question

'The Armada failed because of Spanish mistakes.'

How far do you agree? Explain your answer.

You may use the following in your answer:

- fireships
- Francis Drake.

You **must** also include information of your own.

(16 marks)

Effective conclusions should:

- answer the question directly
- reinforce the judgement made in the essay (without using any new material)
- show why you have chosen a cause / consequence / change / feature over others in the essay
- have a final sentence that links back to the question.

The three key questions in the **skills boosts** will help you to write conclusions effectively.

 1 What are the features of an effective conclusion?

 2 How do I show why one element is more important than others?

3 How do I construct an effective conclusion?

One important feature of an effective conclusion is that it does **not** contain any new information.

Students had the following information available to them to use in answering the exam-style question on page 71.

A Spanish ships could not match English ones in manoeuvrability at the Battle of Gravelines.	**B** The Armada was made up of two fleets (Parma, Medina-Sidonia) that had communications problems.	**C** Knowing England's superior firepower, Nottingham conserved cannonballs for the decisive battle.
D English ships attacked the Armada in the Channel. The Armada was unable to wait for Parma's communications.	**E** Spanish ships could not match English firepower at Gravelines. English cannon fired faster.	**F** Delays meant the Armada had been at sea more than ten weeks. Supplies of food and cannonballs were low.

(1) **a** Amy used evidence B, C, D, E and F in her essay and summarised it in her conclusion. Which of the three conclusions below did she write? ✏️ ....

b Sanjay used evidence A, C, D and E in his essay and summarised it in his conclusion. Which of the three conclusions below did he write? ✏️ ....

Conclusion 1

England's ships were the main reason the Armada was defeated. Spanish ship design meant they were no match for the English. Their less manoeuvrable ships and poorer firepower made it easier for England to win at Gravelines. Almost as important were Philip II ignoring his commanders' concerns and Parma's ships being too small.

Conclusion 2

Overall, the most important reason why the Armada failed was Spain's poor planning and preparations. The English took advantage of communications problems and poor Spanish cannonballs. As English tactics used these weaknesses against Spain, this was also a very important reason the Armada was defeated, but it stems from Spain's preparations.

Conclusion 3

Spanish ships' design played the most important role in England's defeat of the Armada. They were no match against the English, who used their advantages well at Gravelines. This shows that English tactics were also important, and disrupting Spain's communications by attacking Medina-Sidonia in the Channel meant the Spanish were less well-prepared too.

(2) Label ✏️ Amy's and Sanjay's conclusions with the relevant letters A–F to show where their sentences have used the evidence from those cards.

(3) Which conclusion do you think answers the question the most fully? Explain your answer. ✏️

> **Remember:** A conclusion should not introduce new points; it should reinforce points you have already made.

Conclusion .... because ....

....

....

....

....

The Armada

This unit uses the theme of the Armada to build your skills in writing effective conclusions. If you need to review your knowledge of this theme, work through these pages.

1 a Circle Ⓐ which of the following were battles fought with the Spanish Armada.

A | Plymouth

B | Portsmouth

C | Isle of Wight

D | Gravelines

b Circle Ⓐ which of the following were England's naval commanders against the Armada.

A | Sir Walter Raleigh

B | Sir Francis Drake

C | Lord Seymour

D | Earl of Nottingham

c Circle Ⓐ how many ships were in the Armada.

A | 24

B | 56

C | 130

D | 148

d Circle Ⓐ the problems the Armada faced.

A | Rotting food supplies

B | Poor communications

C | Bad weather

D | Poor quality cannonballs

2 The following statements all contain inaccuracies. Write ✎ the correct version below each one.

a Philip II left decisions about tactics to his naval commanders.

....

b Medina-Sidonia's fleet had been at sea for six weeks before it was first sighted in the Channel.

....

c Medina-Sidonia anchored his fleet off the Isle of Wight on 3–4 August 1588.

....

d English fireships destroyed the Spanish fleet at Gravelines.

....

e The English had 124 galleons.

....

f The Duke of Parma's ships were too large to get ready in time.

....

3 Circle (A) the odd one out in each group. Explain (✎) your choice.

a | Medina-Sidonia   Nottingham   Philip II   Parma   Seymour |

....

b | 31 July   6 August   8 August   15 August |

....

c | false retreat   fireships   conserving cannonballs   chasing the Armada |

....

4 Tick (✓) whether each statement is true or false.

		true	false
a	Medina-Sidonia was not ready when Parma sailed into battle at Gravelines.	☐	☐
b	Spanish cannon were faster to reload, but needed more space to fire.	☐	☐
c	The Earl of Nottingham realised that England had an advantage in cannonballs.	☐	☐
d	Medina-Sidonia was unable to rest up off the Isle of Wight.	☐	☐
e	Elizabeth I made a famous victory speech at Tilbury.	☐	☐

5 Draw (✎) lines matching the tops and tails of the following sentences.

tops

A When Spanish ships were boarded the English …

B The Armada had to regroup before Gravelines because …

C The Earl of Nottingham …

D The Duke of Parma …

E Not allowing Medina-Sidonia to anchor off the Isle of Wight meant …

tails

a … realised that the Armada's firepower was inferior to that of the English fleet.

b … Parma did not have time to prepare before Medina-Sidonia's arrival.

c … English fireships scattered the Armada.

d … found rotting supplies.

e … had a lot of small ships that took 48 hours to prepare for battle.

6 How long did it take for word to reach Parma that Medina-Sidonia had arrived in the Channel? (✎)

....

7 Name (✎) **two** ways in which English ship design was better than that of the Spanish when it came to naval battles.

....

....

What are the features of an effective conclusion?

A conclusion must: answer the question directly, reinforce the judgement in the essay and show why you have chosen one element over another. This skills boost will help you to recognise these features.

Exam-style question

'The Armada failed because of the problems Spain had.'

How far do you agree? Explain your answer.

A student answering the question above decided that England's ship design was the main reason why the Armada failed. They wrote the following conclusion.

> Although Spanish problems were quite significant in the failure of the Armada, because they gave England some advantages, such as Parma not being ready for the Battle of Gravelines, England's ship design and tactics were more important. Ship design was most important because it gave England the advantages that enabled its tactics to be used. As English ships had better gun decks, they were able to fire faster than the Spanish at Gravelines. Combined with greater manoeuvrability, this meant that Spain's ships were no match for those of England. England's naval leaders used these differences to inform their tactics, for example saving cannonballs for the final battle, as they knew this advantage would be most important. Spain's problems, such as poor communications, enabled England to make the most of the advantages, but ultimately ship design was the foundation of the English victory.

Remember: You need to show why you have chosen one cause/consequence/change/feature over others in answering your question. This reasoning will inform the judgement you present in your conclusion.

1. a. Highlight 🖉 where the stated factor has been dealt with.

   b. Circle Ⓐ where the most important reason the Armada failed is given.

   c. Underline Ⓐ the reasoning that shows why the most important cause/consequence/change/feature is used.

   d. Double underline Ⓐ where the question is answered directly.

Another student decided that English tactics was the most important reason.

2. a. Circle Ⓐ the statement that gives the judgement about the most important reason why the Armada was defeated.

   A | English tactics to attack Medina-Sidonia's ships made the most of the communications problems Spain had by not giving the Spanish time to prepare Parma's fleet.

   B | English tactics were much more important in the Armada's defeat than Spain's problems.

   C | Spain's poor resources helped but it was the English tactic of conserving cannonballs that enabled it to drive home the advantage when it mattered, at Gravelines.

   b. Highlight 🖉 the phrases that explain why the student chose that reason over the others.

2 How do I show why one element is more important than others?

You will need to show your reasoning for choosing one cause/consequence/change/feature over any others in answering your question. This skills boost will help you to show in your conclusion why you consider one element to be more important than others.

Exam-style question

'The main reason the Armada was defeated was leadership.'

How far do you agree? Explain your answer.

① Which of the statements A–H below link with the following three reasons why the Armada was defeated? ✏ (Some statements might link with more than one reason.)

ⓐ Leadership was the main reason: ....

ⓑ English tactics were the main reason: ....

ⓒ Spain's problems were the main reason: ....

A English ships attacked the Armada in the Channel so communications didn't get through to Parma.	**B** Delays meant the Armada had been at sea for over ten weeks. Supplies of food and cannonballs were low.	**C** Knowing England's superior firepower, Nottingham conserved cannonballs for the decisive battle.
D Drake's 1586 attack on Cadiz severely hampered Spain's preparations.	**E** Parma was not ready for Gravelines as Medina-Sidonia's message was late.	**F** Philip II ignored his naval commanders' suggestions, criticisms and concerns.
G Elizabeth's naval commanders, Drake, Seymour and Nottingham, took key decisions.	**H** Fireships scattered the Spanish fleet, disturbing its preparations for Gravelines.	

② Which of the three reasons do you think had the biggest impact on the failure of the Armada? ✏

....

③ Look at your answer to ②. If you had to pick one statement from A–H above to justify your decision, which would it be and why? ✏

I would choose .... because ....

....

④ On a separate piece of paper, write ✏ your conclusion to answer the exam-style question above. Use this checklist as a guide.

The conclusion does not cover every reason for your judgement; that is done in the essay. Your conclusion uses reasoning to reinforce what led you to choose one element over the others.

Checklist	✓
Answer the question directly. How far was the stated factor the main reason?	
Identify the most important factor.	
Explain why you have chosen one factor over the others.	
Make sure your final sentence links back to the question.	

3 How do I construct an effective conclusion?

An effective conclusion should clearly reinforce your arguments and prove to the reader how convincing they are. This skills boost will help you to structure the features of a successful conclusion.

A | For example, the Armada being split between two fleets led to English decisions to attack Medina-Sidonia in the Channel so it didn't have time to contact Parma.

B | It is more important than English tactics because the naval commanders, Drake, Nottingham and Seymour, made key tactical decisions, like conserving cannonballs and using fireships.

C | Spain's problems were also an important factor, but again, the decisions of English naval commanders made the most of some of them.

D | The most important reason for the failure of the Armada was England's naval commanders.

E | This makes English tactics the second most important factor.

F | Ultimately, without England's commanders, the opportunities presented by the other factors could have been missed.

(1) Sentences **A–F** above are taken from a strong conclusion asking students how far they agree with the statement: 'The most important reason for the failure of the Armada was England's tactics'. The conclusion has all the characteristics listed in the table below. Match the sentences with the characteristics listed in the table, and write 🖉 the letters **A–F** in the right-hand column.

Key characteristics of an effective conclusion	Which statement shows which characteristic? 🖉
a Statement giving what you believe to be the most important factor	
b Statement on how far you agree with the stated factor	
c Explain your case for your choice of most important factor and why it is more important than any other factors	
d Bring in the relative importance of any other factors	
e Reinforce your conclusion about the most important factor and how it relates to the stated factor and other factors	
f Statement giving what you believe to be the most important factor	

(2) Now put 🖉 sentences A–F into the correct order to form a coherent conclusion.

(3) **a** Underline Ⓐ the sentences (A–F) where the student gives a reason for the failure.

b Circle Ⓐ where the student has addressed the issue of how far the stated factor is to blame.

Sample response

Knowing how to write an effective conclusion is very important in convincing the reader of the arguments you presented. Knowing the difference between an effective and ineffective conclusion will help you when it comes to writing your own.

A student using the information from page 72 wrote the following conclusion to this exam-style question:

Exam-style question

'The main reason for the defeat of the Armada was English tactics.'

How far do you agree? Explain your answer.

English tactics enabled the English fleet to make the most of its advantages, such as superior ship design and Spain's problems. It was Spain's problems, however, that gave England some of its most important advantages. Communications not getting through led to Parma not being ready for Gravelines, which helped maximise England's tactical advantage in ship design. Also, Spain's poor supplies of cannonballs maximised England's advantage in firepower at Gravelines. England's naval leaders recognised the advantages Spain's problems gave them and they devised their tactics accordingly: English tactics relied upon Spain's problems.

(1) Which factor does the student say was the most important?

....

(2) Underline (A) the reasoning the student uses to show why this factor was so important.

(3) Other than the stated and most important factors, which other element does the conclusion mention?

....

(4) Why does the student think English tactics are less important than Spain's problems?

....

The student's conclusion could be stronger. To be effective, their paragraph needs to start by answering the question directly and giving the judgement. It also needs a final sentence linking back to the question.

(5) Write the opening 2–3 sentences of a conclusion in answer to the exam-style question above.

....

....

....

....

(6) Write a final sentence that rounds off the answer, linking back to the question.

....

....

Your turn!

'The main reason for the defeat of the Armada was English tactics.'

How far do you agree? Explain your answer.

You may use the following in your answer:

- Francis Drake
- ship design.

You **must** also use information of your own.

(16 marks)

(1) Use the information below to write ✐ a conclusion to the question. As well as the stated factor, the other two to think about are **leadership** and **Spain's problems**.

a	Spanish ships could not match English ships in manoeuvrability at the Battle of Gravelines.
b	Spanish ships could not match English ships in firepower at Gravelines. English cannon fired faster.
c	Philip II ignored his naval commanders' suggestions, tactics, criticisms and concerns.
d	Elizabeth let her naval commanders make all the key decisions.
e	As England had superior firepower, Nottingham saved cannonballs for the decisive battle.
f	English ships attacked Medina-Sidonia in the Channel, disrupting communications with Parma.
g	Fireships scattered the Spanish fleet, disturbing its preparations for Gravelines.
h	Delays meant the Armada was at sea for over ten weeks. Supplies of food and cannonballs were low.
i	Due to communication problems, Parma was not ready for the Battle of Gravelines.

Do not attempt to include all of the information above in the conclusion. Use only the information that best helps you to explain your reasoning.
- Answer the question directly. How far was the stated element the main reason?
- Identify the most important element.
- Explain why you have chosen one element over the others.
- Make sure your final sentence links back to the question.

....

....

....

....

....

....

....

....

....

....

Review your skills

Check up

Review your response to the exam-style question on page 79. Tick ✓ the column to show how well you think you have done each of the following.

	Had a go ✓	Nearly there ✓	Got it! ✓
understood the features of an effective conclusion	☐	☐	☐
shown in the conclusion how one element is more important than others	☐	☐	☐
summarised and reinforced my arguments to construct an effective conclusion	☐	☐	☐

Look over all of your work in this unit. Note down 🖊 three things you have learned that you will apply when writing an effective conclusion.

① ....

② ....

③ ....

Need more practice?

On separate paper, plan and write 🖊 your response to the exam-style question below.

Exam-style question

'The main reason for the plots against Elizabeth I was religion.'

How far do you agree? Explain your answer.

You may use the following in your answer:

- the Revolt of the Northern Earls
- Philip II.

You **must** also use information of your own.

(16 marks)

How confident do you feel about each of these **skills**? Colour 🖊 in the bars.

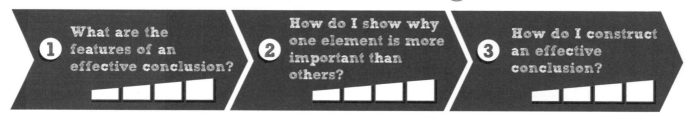

1 What are the features of an effective conclusion?

2 How do I show why one element is more important than others?

3 How do I construct an effective conclusion?

Answers

Unit 1

Page 2

(1) (a), (b), (c) and (d)

Justices of the Peace were vital to local government. They reported to the Privy Council and made sure that all social and economic policies were carried out in their areas. | Being a JP was a popular role because it was a position of status, although it was unpaid. JPs also heard serious crimes at county courts every three months. They were often gentry, who were near the top of the Elizabethan social hierarchy but below the nobility.

Page 3

(1) A = c, i; B = a, h; C = b, d; D = f; E = e, g, j

(2) Student's own response, but it should include two of the following:
- Declare war and make peace
- Call and dismiss parliament
- Reject any laws parliament had voted for
- Rule in some legal cases if the law was unclear or people appealed a judgement
- Patronage – grant titles, land, money, jobs

(3) (a) false
  (b) false
  (c) false
  (d) false
  (e) true
  (f) true

Page 4

(4) (a) Philip II. The others were all potential husbands/ suitors for Elizabeth I.

  (b) subsidies. The others were all ways of raising money without calling parliament.

  (c) merchants. The others were all social groups in rural society.

(5) (a) Francis Walsingham was not Elizabeth I's most important privy councillor and he did not become Lord Burghley. Both were William Cecil.

  Correct statement: Elizabeth I's most important privy councillor was William Cecil, who became Lord Burghley in 1573. *Or:* Francis Walsingham was Elizabeth I's secretary of state from 1573.

  (b) Vagrancy *was* discussed by parliament. The third issue Elizabeth I did not want parliament to discuss was foreign policy.

  Correct statement: Three subjects that Elizabeth I did not want parliament to discuss were foreign policy, her marriage and the succession. *Or:* Vagrancy was discussed by parliament whereas Elizabeth I's marriage and the succession were not.

  (c) The Auld Alliance was between Scotland and France. The Treaty of Cateau-Cambrésis ended the conflict between France and Spain in 1559.

  Correct statement: The Treaty of Cateau-Cambrésis was the agreement that ended the war between Spain and France in 1559. *Or:* The Auld Alliance was an old agreement between Scotland and France to deter English invasions.

(6) B

(7) B

Page 5

(1) A and B are key features with many examples. C is not a key feature. D and E are key features with long-term trends.

(2) When Elizabeth I called parliament in 1572, after the Ridolfi Plot, she was most displeased that they called for the execution of Mary, Queen of Scots. The role of Elizabethan parliaments was to offer advice, not make demands of the queen. The only time Elizabeth I requested its advice was in the session called from October 1586 to March 1587, when she asked for its view on Mary's execution. Otherwise parliament was expected simply to pass laws for the queen and grant extraordinary taxation. When Peter Wentworth demanded free speech for MPs in 1576, the Commons itself sent him to the Tower of London.

Page 6

(1) (a) B, D and E all have relevant and specific facts. Both B and D give one of many examples of privy councillors (B) and ways in which the Privy Council was involved with England's law and order (D). C is a statement about an individual councillor, not a key feature.

  (b) B and D

	Relevant	Specific	One of many examples
A The Privy Council met frequently	✓		
B Elizabeth I often chose councillors who were new, Protestant nobles like the Earl of Leicester	✓	✓	✓
C Sir William Cecil was Elizabeth I's most significant privy councillor			
D The Privy Council played an important part in England's law and order, such as monitoring JPs	✓	✓	✓
E Elizabeth I's Privy Council had approximately 19 members	✓	✓	
F Elizabeth I often presided over Privy Council meetings	✓		

(2) **a** and **b**

One key feature of Elizabeth I's Privy Council was its close links to local government. For example, it monitored the work of JPs, who were responsible for implementing the government's social and economic policies, and keeping law and order. ~~JPs were usually large landowners.~~

Page 7

(1) **a**, **b** and **c**

Feature 1: One key feature was that Mary, Queen of Scots, was also Queen of France. Her mother was Mary of Guise. The Guise were an important, noble, Catholic family that was very powerful and influential in the French court. This meant that the French could threaten England from both north and south at the same time. ~~Mary, Queen of Scots, was Catholic and had a legitimate claim to the English throne, so she could expect support from Catholic France if she pursued her claim.~~

Feature 2: France and Spain had ended their conflict and signed the Treaty of Cateau-Cambrésis. Spain and France were very powerful countries and traditional enemies. They had been at war during the 1550s and England, under Mary I and Philip II, had sided with Spain. All the while Spain and France were rivals, England was safer, but now there was a real possibility that these two Catholic nations might unite against the Protestant English queen. <u>Protestantism was a Christian religion that rejected a lot of Catholic teaching.</u>

d Student's own response.

Page 8

(1) Feature 1, Strengths:
- Gives a clear key feature: 'Each county had a Lord Lieutenant …'
- Gives specific supporting detail: '… vital to maintaining the monarch's powers as they oversaw defence and raised local militia'

Feature 1, Weaknesses:
- Explains what the militia was, which isn't necessary: 'The militia was a force of ordinary people raised in an emergency.'
- Unnecessary additional key feature added: 'Lords Lieutenant were chosen by the monarch to ensure the enforcement of her policies.'

Feature 2, Strengths:
- Gives a clear key feature: 'The monarch was probably the most important part of the government as she was its head.'
- Strong, specific supporting detail, for example: 'They could rule in some legal cases if the judgement was unclear, or if someone appealed to them …'

Feature 2, Weaknesses:
- Unnecessary description – it is not a question on Elizabeth I's key features as monarch: 'As a monarch, Elizabeth I was highly intelligent, confident but indecisive.'
- There are three pieces of supporting detail, which is more than is necessary for the 2 marks: 'Only the monarch had the power to declare war and make peace. They could rule in some legal cases if the judgement was unclear, or if someone appealed to them, and they could call and dismiss parliament.'

Page 9

(1) Student's own response, but an answer might be formed from the suggestions below:

Key feature	Supporting evidence
Elizabethan society was a hierarchy.	Landless, labouring poor were the bulk of the population and at the base, whereas gentry and nobility were very few and at the top.
Elizabethan society was not based on equality/was based on inequality.	It was believed females ought to be under the authority of males; the majority of the population were poor (e.g. unskilled workers and unemployed) with a very few rich at the top (e.g. merchants).
The more land people held in Elizabethan society, the higher up the social scale they were.	Nobility and gentry at the top held vast estates; at the bottom were the landless, vagrants and homeless.
A duty of care was owed to those below you in the social structure.	Landowners were expected to take care of tenants, especially during times of hardship.

(2) This will depend on the student's own response, but should use the suggestions on page 8.

Unit 2

Page 12

(1) **a** One reason for opposition to the Elizabethan religious settlement was that clergy had to wear vestments. ~~Vestments are special clothes worn by the clergy. They were often quite elaborate.~~ Puritans believed this was wrong as it suggested the clergy were special. ~~Puritans were extreme Protestants who wanted to purify the Church of anything~~ ~~Catholic or not in the Bible.~~ Catholics believed priests performed the miracle of transubstantiation during Mass, ~~meaning the bread and wine became the body and blood of Christ,~~ and so were special. ~~Protestants and Puritans thought this was wrong and caused some opposition as the Royal Injunctions said clergy had to wear vestments, but plainer than Catholic ones.~~ Many Puritan clergy refused to wear vestments. Matthew Parker published the 'Book of Advertisements' showing what priests ought to wear and held an exhibition in London. He invited 110 clergy but 37 refused to attend and lost their posts. This shows that although the religious settlement was Protestant, it was still too Catholic for some.

b B; because it is unnecessary description
E is not necessary
G; because it repeats point A

H; because it is on the strength of opposition, not why there was opposition. It gives information that is not relevant to the question.

Page 13

①

What it was	What it did
Act of Supremacy	Made Elizabeth I head of the Church of England; all clergy had to swear an oath of loyalty to her
Act of Uniformity	Established the appearances of churches and the form of services
Royal Injunctions	Reinforced the Acts of Supremacy and Uniformity. Three things from the Royal Injunctions: student's own response, but they should choose from: • all clergy were to teach the royal supremacy • anyone who refused to attend church should be reported to the Privy Council • each parish was to have a copy of the Bible in English • no one was to preach without a licence from the government • forbade pilgrimages and monuments to 'fake' miracles • clergy were to wear special vestments.

② A Durham = **a** Strongly Catholic
B Essex = **c** Some Protestant support
C Kent = **c** Some Protestant support
D Lancashire = **a** Strongly Catholic
E London = **d** Strongly Protestant
F Suffolk = **c** Some Protestant support
None of the places listed could be described as **b** Some Catholic support.

③ Catholic: a, c, e, f, h; Protestant: b, d, g

Page 14

④ Student's own response, but they could include any of the following:

Puritans were much stricter than other Protestants; Puritans saw no role for the monarch as head of the Church, whereas other Protestants did; Puritans did not believe that priests should wear special vestments, whereas other Protestants did (as long as they were not ornate like Catholic vestments); Puritans did not like altars, whereas other Protestants did.

⑤ 1 = C; 2 = F; 3 = D; 4 = E; 5 = B; 6 = A

⑥ a = recusant
b = 8,000
c = 1 shilling
d = 27

⑦ B and D

⑧ A, B and D

Page 15

① A, B, D, F and G should be highlighted.

② There was Catholic opposition to the Elizabeth I's Protestant religious settlement on several points. One was the miracle that Catholics believed took place during Mass, when the bread and wine became the body and blood of Christ [D]. For Protestants, it was simply a reminder of the last time that Christ shared bread and wine with his disciples [A]. Another point was cutting the number of church services in which there was a holy presence that gave God's blessing [B] from seven to two. Protestants only recognised Baptism and Holy Communion. There was also opposition to the oath accepting Elizabeth I as the Governor of the Church [C].

In 1558 England's bishops were all Catholic and only one took the oath. After the first inspections to make sure the Elizabethan religious settlement was being followed [E], 400 clergy were dismissed, though not all were Catholic.

Page 16

① B, as it clearly focuses on the question and gives a reason why there was opposition.

② Statement A is not a good way to start the paragraph on the vestments controversy because it is describing the difference between Puritans and other Protestants rather than making a relevant point that is focused on the question.

③ Unnecessary description: a, c; Not focused on the question: d

④ Student's own response, but the strongest combination would be: B; e, f, g.

Page 17

① One reason for opposition to the religious settlement was that clergy had to take an oath agreeing to the Royal Supremacy. For Catholics, the only spiritual leader was the pope, God's representative on Earth. So, this part of the settlement was a step too far. England's bishops were all Catholic when Elizabeth I became queen. All but one refused the oath. Although most of the lower clergy were also Catholic, the majority took it. Protestants did not believe there should be a pope, so it was not an issue for them. So, the Royal Supremacy led to some opposition but nothing that seriously affected it.

② Why the appearance of churches led to puritan opposition.

③ Appearance of churches and clergy → opposition. Puritans wanted simple churches, Elizabeth I thought crucifixes important to reassure Catholics. Royal Supremacy meant she was head of Church, so could keep crucifixes. Catholics liked decorated churches. Some Puritan bishops threatened to resign. They'd been in the Netherlands, where Protestantism was strong.

Crucifixes = against Puritan idea that plain churches → fewer distractions from worshipping God.

Page 18

1

Strengths		Weaknesses	
Paragraph opens with a clear point about why there was opposition.	2	Paragraph contains information that is unnecessary or irrelevant (filler).	1 & 2
Paragraph ends with a clear link back to the question.	1	Paragraph wanders off the question focus.	1 & 2
A reason why there was opposition is clearly explained with relevant evidence.	1 & 2	Paragraph contains unnecessary explanation of historical terms.	1

2 Student's own response, but ought to be 4/6.

Page 19

1 Student's own response, but here is one option:

It is hard to identify why there was Catholic opposition to the religious settlement before 1569, as Elizabeth I did not want recusants punished. There was clearly some Catholic opposition at first, as all but one bishop refused to take the oath of supremacy to Elizabeth I as head of the Church in 1559. Some lesser clergy refused to take it, but about 8,000 did out of 10,000 parishes in England. So a large majority of lesser clergy took the oath. There were religious divisions in England too, with the North and West being more Catholic and London, Kent and East Anglia more Protestant.

There was serious opposition from Catholics in northern England in 1569. It is not possible to say that it was all about religion, but for the ordinary people taking part it was a protest against the religious settlement. The new Bishop of Durham, James Pilkington, a strict Protestant, was very unpopular. The rebels carried Catholic banners and held Mass in Durham. The rebellion's leaders were northern earls from ancient Catholic families. However, they had other reasons for rebelling, not just religion. So, ordinary Catholics in northern England clearly rebelled against the new Protestant service.

Unit 3

Page 22

1

How well does each plan ...	Very well	Quite well	Not at all
show a wide variety of reasons?	A	B	
show how one cause leads to another, and so on?	B		A
show how causes interact with each other?		B	A

Page 23

1 B, D, F, H

2 **a** true

b true

c false

d false

e false

f true

g true

3 A = b; B = c; C = b; D = a; E = b, c; F = b

4 Poor relief was money given to the poor; the poor rate was a tax paid by the better-off to provide relief for the poor.

Page 24

5 Correct order = b, e, d, c, a

6 A = c; B = a; C = d; D = b

7 **a** 1579–83; because the other periods are all downturns in the cloth trade

b providing unemployed with raw materials; because it comes from the 1576 Poor Relief Act and the others come from the 1572 Vagabonds Act

c impotent; because they were seen as being the deserving poor

d skilled labour; because all the other categories were unskilled and so more likely to suffer from poverty

8 C

Page 25

1 Student's own response, but it needs to be a logical sequence. Examples could include:

E was caused by K, D, J

I was caused by K, C, D

Note: If C or K is chosen, column 1 will be blank (C was caused by international factors outside England and K is a root cause of vagrancy); if G is chosen, column 3 will be blank (G led directly to vagrancy).

2 Student's own response, but might include:

K → I → B → G

K → A → D → J → H → G

Page 26

1 A There was more unemployment because the population grew. Vagrancy increased as people lost their homes, causing them to wander the countryside. Without work they couldn't afford their rents leading to vagrancy.

B Secondly, the shortage of jobs caused wages to fall. Employers could pay less because there were plenty of unemployed people willing to take any work they could get. Falling wages often resulted in severe poverty, meaning people consequently could not afford their rents, leading to homelessness. A direct consequence of this was that people ended up wandering the countryside or heading to cities hoping for a better life.

② Strengths	A, B or both?	Weaknesses	A, B or both?
Clear focus to the paragraph	B	Paragraph focus uncertain	A
Causation is explained	B	A series of statements about cause	A
Specific supporting evidence	B	Undeveloped historical knowledge	A

③ There is more than one solution as far as the words to build a causal argument are concerned. One suggestion is: England's population grew by 35% during Elizabeth I's reign **causing** the supply of labour **to** increase. **Consequently** unemployment and vagrancy grew worse, for example when the cloth trade was bad in 1568–73 it **led to** the government passing the 1572 Vagabonds Act.

Page 27

① Student's own response, but A, J, H, E and F have the greatest impact. Enclosure affected only 2–3% of the land, suggesting that sheep farming was not a big reason either.

② Student's own response, depending on what has been chosen, but A is a root cause.

③ B is the best choice as it gives the key points in the causal chain. A goes through the whole causal process again and is unnecessary; C is too vague.

Page 28

① Plan A is the better plan because it:
- clearly shows causation
- combines causation with evidence to develop a causal argument
- has strong links back to the question
- highlights other important causes.

Plan B has a lot of information, but also paragraphs that simply string a lot of causes together.

Page 29

① Student's own response.

Unit 4

Page 32

① A = a, b, d; B = a, c, and g; C = a, possibly b, d; D = b, d; E = a, e, f

② Student's own response, but ought to include some from each of the following:
A = a, b, c, f, h; B = e, possibly f, g; C = a, b, c, d, f, h; D = a, b, possibly c; E = b, c, d, f, h; F = a, b, c, f, possibly h; G = e, g; H = a, b, c, e, f, h

Page 33

① Student's own response, but could include two from:
Mary, Queen of Scots, had a potentially stronger claim to the English throne than Elizabeth I; Mary, Queen of Scots' claim had no issue of legitimacy; she was married to the French king and was Queen of Scotland so had

Elizabeth I surrounded; the Auld Alliance; she was a Catholic alternative to Elizabeth I.

②
1568	Mary, Queen of Scots' arrival in England
1569–70	Revolt of the Northern Earls
1570	Papal bull of excommunication
1571	Ridolfi Plot
1574	Catholic priests began arriving in England
1583–84	Throckmorton Plot
1586	Babington Plot
1587	Execution of Mary, Queen of Scots
1588	Spanish Armada

③
a Revolt of the Northern Earls; because all the other plots were intercepted and stopped before anything happened.

b Sussex; because he fought for/was loyal to Elizabeth I in the Revolt of the Northern Earls. The others were involved in the plot against her.

c Wiretapping; because all the others were methods used to obtain information on Elizabeth I's enemies.

d Cecil; because he was loyal to Elizabeth I; the others were not; *or* he increased his influence at court; the others did not

e Philip II of Spain was a king and the others weren't is true – but too obvious (worth ¼ mark). The Duke of Guise was the only one *not* involved in the Ridolfi Plot.

Page 34

④ Ridolfi 1571 = A, C

Throckmorton 1583–84 = E, G (the Duke of Guise was involved)

Babington 1586 = B, D, E, F, G (by this time the Treaty of Joinville had been signed and the King of France was under the influence of the Guise and Philip II)

⑤ Student's own response, but answers should be along the lines of:

Although Elizabeth I was not assassinated there was enough evidence of Mary, Queen of Scots' role in the plot to hold a trial and convict her, in accordance with the Act of Parliament. She was found guilty of treason and the sentence had to be execution.

⑥ A, B, C

⑦ B, D

⑧ A, B, D

Page 35

① **Religious context 1580s:**
No change

Political context 1580s:
Mary = Catholic with strong claim to English throne

Bigger threat, although no change in her claim (international situation: England at war with Spain)

Mary captive in England

No change

Plots against Elizabeth I

No change (Plots continue: Throckmorton, Babington not really more serious than Ridolfi)

International context 1580s:
Anglo-Spanish relations = tense

Deteriorating: Drakes' voyages angered Philip II; Treaty of Nonsuch led to England promising to help Dutch rebels; England and Spain at war (Armada).

Spain and France = rivals

Changed: Spain and France = allies (Treaty of Joinville)

England intervening unofficially in the Netherlands

Important change: Treaty of Nonsuch meant England was involved in the Netherlands

(2) Mary, Queen of Scots, was more of a threat in 1587 because Anglo-Spanish relations had deteriorated into war, France and Spain had become allies and Philip II was planning the Armada.

Page 36

(1) The changes in the way Catholics were treated came in the 1580s (1581 onwards).

(2)

Date	Change in context
1569	Revolt of the Northern Earls; after Mary, Queen of Scots, had come to England in 1568 – rebellion focused on marrying her to Norfolk
1571	Papal bull 1570; Ridolfi Plot
1581	Spain gains Portugal; making progress in the Netherlands
1585	Deaths of Alençon and William of Orange; Treaty of Joinville (1584); Treaty of Nonsuch. All of which put England in danger as Spain and France were allies and England was now officially intervening in the Netherlands to support Dutch Protestants
1586–87	Babington Plot; Philip II building his Armada against England

(3) Student's own response, but could mention: deteriorating relations with Spain; Spain and France becoming allies as Roman Catholic countries against heresy, and as England officially sides with the Dutch Protestants; also by the time of the Babington Plot, it was clear that Philip II was building his Armada against England.

Page 37

(1)

Domestic context	1560s	1580s
Elizabeth I and religious settlement = Protestant	✓	✓
Pope = alternative source of authority for English Catholics	✓	✓
Mary, Queen of Scots, captive in England; strong claim to throne	✓	✓
Catholic plots failed	✓	✓
International context	1560s	1580s
All of the Netherlands was rebelling against Spanish rule	✓	✓
A large Spanish army was in the Netherlands	✓	✓
Spain and France were rivals	✓	
Philip II was planning to invade England		✓

(2) (a) Student's own response, but likely to be 3 (quite significant), as the domestic context itself was not much different, e.g. the religious settlement was still Protestant, Mary, Queen of Scots, was still a problem, there were continuing plots around Mary, Queen of Scots, although two in quick succession. Arguably a higher score if students point out that the international context impacted on the domestic one, making English Catholics seem more threatening – resulting in the increasingly harsh treatment of Catholics in England.

(b) Student's own response. Likely to be 2 (very significant), possibly 1 (highly significant). The obvious change is the Franco-Spanish alliance, isolating England as a Protestant nation. 1587 also marks the execution of Mary, Queen of Scots (some students might remember that this came on top of rumours that Spanish troops had landed in Wales), a huge change in Elizabeth I's reaction. The domestic context was not much different – the international context had changed, however.

(3) Student's own response.

(4) Student's own response.

Page 38

(1) (a), (b), (c) and (d)

If Mary, Queen of Scots' claim to the throne had been the reason for her execution, then she would have been executed much earlier. For example, Norfolk was a threat to the throne and was executed after the Ridolfi Plot, but Mary was not. The Ridolfi Plot involved the Spanish and had papal approval. The pope had issued his papal bull against Elizabeth I the year before. This made all English Catholics suspect, thus changing the domestic context of the Catholic threat as Elizabeth I was no longer certain of their loyalty. However, Mary was not executed until 1587.

By 1587, circumstances had changed greatly*. England was more under threat from Catholicism than at any time previously. This was reflected in laws and actions against English Catholics becoming much harsher, and Mary's execution in 1587. By 1585, the international context had changed significantly*. France and Spain had allied against heresy, and England and Spain were at war. An invasion by 1586 to restore Catholicism and put Mary on the throne was expected as Philip prepared his Armada. Mary's claim to the throne was the same, but the changing international context made it look like it could now succeed. Catholics in England were more suspect than ever. Therefore, Mary, Queen of Scots, had to be executed after the Babington Plot. The actual plot was no more serious than any other, and got no further.

(e) Student's own response.

Page 39

(1) Student's own response.

Unit 5

Page 42

(1)

Wingina as a cause	The colonists as a cause	Chance events
G, I, J	B, C, E, F, H	A, D

② The role of the colonists (or possibly 'luck' – depending on how deeply students are thinking)

③ E

④ A, B, C, D and F also explain why the colonists relied so much on Wingina; G suggests that Wingina was willing to help at first.

⑤ Student's own response. It is likely that students haven't changed their opinion or have changed their response to 'Very little'.

Page 43

① A = d; B = a; C = e; D = c; E = b

② ⓐ A
   ⓑ A, B
   ⓒ C
   ⓓ B

Page 44

③ ⓐ false
   ⓑ false
   ⓒ true
   ⓓ true
   ⓔ false
   ⓕ true
   ⓖ false

④ Student's own response, from: women/families went as well; the new colonists were poor people from London, who were used to hardship; they were guaranteed 500 acres of land; a Native American – Manteo – was the leader

⑤ 1 = J; 2 = F; 3 = E; 4 = D; 5 = B; 6 = L; 7 = G; 8 = A; 9 = H; 10 = I; 11 = C; 12 = K

Page 45

① ⓐ Chance events = A, F; Poor planning = A (all important supplies were on one ship); B, C, D
   ⓑ Student's own response, for example, 'The colonists themselves' (evidence B, C, D, E, F) and 'Wingina' or 'Native Americans' would work (evidence E, F, G, H).

② Student's own response, depending on the categories they have chosen.

③ D = Yes, probably or Maybe; E = Maybe (some did survive the winter) or No way; H = Maybe or Yes, probably (if there had been no conflict)

④ Student's own response, depending on how they are argued, but A would have made a huge difference; B and A together could have seen a very different outcome.

⑤ Student's own response.

Page 46

①

Problems faced by the first colony (1585)	Problems faced by the second colony (1587)
Poor planning – wrong mix of colonists, arrived too late to plant crops	
Bad luck	
First attempt, so colonists were inexperienced	

Wingina	
Violent clashes between Native Americans and settlers	✓
Poor leadership – for example, Grenville and Lane did not get on	Possibly – Manteo attacked wrong tribe

② ⓐ Student's own response, but likely to be poor planning (setting sail too late) or luck (vital supplies lost).
   ⓑ Student's own response, but likely to be hostility of Native Americans; or possibly poor leadership because of Manteo's mistake, but hostility that led to Howe's murder came first.

③ Student's own response. There should be a clear judgement on the significant causes of both, plus supporting evidence.

Page 47

① Likely to be Wingina as he was more directly to blame; some might decide Raleigh because of poor planning, but based on what is presented in the table and no other knowledge, it's Wingina.

② ⓐ **Chief Wingina** impacted on the colonists by denying them help and turning against them. He had no impact on the planning or chance events.

   The colonists had an impact on Wingina by demanding more and more from him, which turned him against them; the colonists had no impact on the planning of the expedition (masterminded by Raleigh) or chance events.

   The planning of the expedition impacted on Wingina, as the colonists came to rely on him for help, having left too late to plant crops and most of their supplies having been put in one ship that ran aground. It impacted on the colonists as it left them without the means to survive; the choice of colonists was also poor planning; it impacted upon the chance events as, had supplies been spread around different ships, anything unfortunate happening to one (and those journeys were very dangerous) would not have had too big an impact.

   Chance events impacted upon the colonists, by depriving them of the means to survive; it also impacted on Wingina as the diseases unwittingly brought by the colonists led him to think they were supernatural and so he trusted them even less. It had no impact on the planning of the expedition.

   ⓑ The planning of the expedition.

Page 48

①

Has the answer ...	A	B	C
clearly highlighted the most significant cause?			✓
supported it with specific evidence?		✓	✓
shown how it impacted on other factors?		✓*	✓
shown any change of significant factor over time?		✓**	✓

*Inasmuch as there is a clearly highlighted most significant cause.

**The answer does show different factors as significant, but it is not very clear.

Page 49

(1) Student's own response.

(2) Student's own response.

Unit 6

Page 52

(1) **(a)** and **(b)**

Intro

Overview of the aims of Drake's three voyages (circumnavigation, raiding Spanish New World territories, attacking Spanish navy in Cadiz)

Paragraph 1

~~Circumnavigation 1577–80. Aim = be first English person to sail around world (although there is some doubt about this being his main aim).~~
~~Also, to make money and raid Spanish colonies.~~
~~Plus explain why Elizabeth I wanted revenge on Spain – Anglo-Spanish relations deteriorating~~

Paragraph 2

Nova Albion – what/where was it; coronation ceremony
Drake returned with huge sums of money but only 1 ship and 56 men
Elizabeth I knighted Drake, making Philip II furious

Paragraph 3

~~1585: Elizabeth I sent Drake to raid Spanish New World colonies to disrupt Philip II's flow of resources.~~ Philip II angered by yet more of Drake's raids on top of others.
This voyage probably persuaded Philip II to go ahead with Armada.

Paragraph 4

England and Spain at war. Drake's raid was daring and he attacked Spanish navy over 3 days, destroyed 30 ships, known as 'singeing of the King of Spain's beard' – bound to anger Philip II. Plus, Drake went on to the New World.

Conclusion

Yes – Drake's voyages made Philip II angry.

(2) Strongly (3/4 paragraphs)

Page 53

(1) Drake: B = b, C = c and D = a
Hawkins: A = f; B = b
Raleigh: E = d; F = e; G = g

(2) **(a)** B
(b) D
(c) B
(d) A
(e) A, B, C, D

(3)

Consequence	Immediate (short-term)	Long-term	Intended	Unintended
A Only 56 survivors returned	✓			✓
B English ships and sailors proven among the best in the world		✓	✓*	
C Raleigh sent a factfinding mission to Virginia		✓	✓	

*This could be arguable, but as only one other person had done it before, this can't really be unexpected (unintended).

Page 54

(3) **(a)** In 1585, Elizabeth I sent Drake to raid Spain's New World ports.

(b) The consequence of Drake's 1585 voyage was that Philip II decided to invade England.

(c) In April 1587, Drake sailed into Cadiz harbour and destroyed 30 Spanish ships.

(d) The raid on Cadiz harbour delayed the Armada by a year.

(e) After attacking Cadiz, Drake sailed to Portugal and the Azores to attack Spanish treasure ships.

(f) By giving England more time to prepare for the Armada, which was defeated, Drake's attack on Cadiz made Elizabeth I more secure on the throne.

(4) 1 = B; 2 = D; 3 = A; 4 = C

(5) **(a)** California; because it was the only one where England made any colonial claims.

(b) establish an English colony; because the others were all reasons behind Drake's circumnavigation.

(c) Golden Hind; because all the others sailed on the first colonisation of Virginia in 1585.

Page 55

(1) **(a)** A, H, I

(b) B, C, D, E, F, G, J

(2) **(a)** and **(b)**

Drake made three important voyages between 1577 and 1587, each of which angered Philip II. Throughout this time, (Anglo-Spanish relations were deteriorating, and Drake's voyages also led) to this. Elizabeth I wanted to disrupt Philip II's flows of resources from the New World. This was why Drake's 1585 voyage was so important: because (it disrupted Philip II's flows of resources from the New World) when England and Spain were at war. Philip II was so angry that this voyage triggered the building of the Armada. The 1587 voyage was even more important as (it gave England time to prepare defences against the Armada), which it defeated.

(c) Consequences for exploration (C) and for Drake and the investors (D, E, J).

Page 56

(1) The only one that is **not** a consequence is E, England and the Netherlands signed the Treaty of Nonsuch

(2) A → H → C

Though, there are other possible solutions.

Page 57

1. Student's own response. Likely to be D leads to A leads to C.

2. Student's own response. Likely to be F in terms of quantity and quality of consequences, given that the question requires consideration of the impact on Elizabethan England.

3. **1577 circumnavigation:**

   Positive A, B, C, E

   Negative D

   Short-term A, D (arguable)

   Long-term E, B, C

   1586 raids

   Positive B, C, D, E

   Negative A (arguable)

   Short-term A, B, C, D

   Long-term E (arguable)

4. Student's own response, but likely still to be 1587. Explanation should consider impact of consequences.

Page 58

1. Drake's voyages had the very important consequence for his investors of making huge profits. For example, in 1572 he returned with £40,000 from Panama and in 1580 he returned with £400,000 – ten times that. This prompted further exploration of North America.

   Another reason why voyages of exploration to the New World were undertaken was that adventure was important to Elizabethan gentlemen. More important, however, was to raid Spain's New World colonies and disrupt Philip II's flow of wealth and resources. Elizabeth I made this clear to Drake in her secret orders before he set off for his circumnavigation. In fact, Drake's circumnavigation is often said to be an unintended consequence of what was supposed to be another privateering expedition against the Spanish.

   Although Philip II was angered* by Elizabeth I's knighting of Drake in 1580, the decision to build an Armada was the consequence of Drake's 1585 raids on Spanish New World colonies. By this time the international context had changed. England and Spain were at war, which made Philip II's anger* as a result of this latest raid a far more significant consequence than it had been in 1580. Drake's raids, ordered by Elizabeth I, had now resulted in seriously endangering England.

   It was another consequence of one of Drake's raids, however, that lessened the danger. This was in April 1587. The ultimate outcome was the defeat of the Armada.

Page 59

1. Student's own response – although it should follow the guidelines.

2. Student's own response.

Unit 7

Page 62

1. a 1 piece (statement 1).

   b Not very important.

   c Religion: 5 pieces of evidence (2, 3, 4, 5, 6) = very important.

   Court politics: 2 pieces of evidence (5, 7) = not very important.

   Overthrow Elizabeth I: 1 piece of evidence (statement 2) = not very important.

2. Religion

3. Only looks at quantity, not quality.

Page 63

1. a B, C, E

   b A, C, D, E

   c B

   d A

2. a false

   b false

   c true

   d false

   e true

   f false

3. James Pilkington

Page 64

4. a London; because the rebels captured all the others.

   b Earl of Huntingdon; because all the others were involved in the plot at one time or another.

   c Duke of Alençon; because all the others were issues concerning the rebels.

5. a The papal bull excommunicating Elizabeth I was an important consequence of the rebellion.

   b The Earl of Northumberland was captured and executed. or: the Earl of Westmorland escaped.

   c After the rebellion, 450 rebels were executed across northern England.

   d Elizabeth I sent a Protestant/someone less sympathetic to Catholics to govern northern England.

6. 1 = E; 2 = G; 3 = B; 4 = C; 5 = A; 6 = D; 7 = F

Page 65

1. Evidence suggesting the succession was important: 1

   Evidence linking the succession to other causes: 2

   Evidence suggesting the succession was not important: 3, 4, 5, 6, 7

2. Student's own response.

3. Student's own response.

Page 66

(1) **a** A focuses on the succession whereas C sees replacing Elizabeth as the main aim so that a wider range of objectives can be met, such as getting rid of the likes of Cecil and Leicester.

b Ordinary rebels did not concern themselves with politics.

(2) **a** Student's own response, but an example is: Although the aim of a change in government was important to the northern earls, religion was more important to the ordinary rebels.

b Student's own response, but an example is: While the succession was more important when the rebellion began, religion became more important as the rebellion developed.

Page 67

(1) Northern earls were from ancient Catholic nobility. They had lost influence at court under Elizabeth I to new, Protestant men, e.g. Cecil, Leicester. Political rivalry = important and partly based on religion.

Plot began with aim of securing an heir for Elizabeth I by marrying Mary, Queen of Scots, to Norfolk, but developed into replacing Elizabeth I with Catholic Mary. Succession was not very important. Shows the plot was political, but also religious as it was about having a Catholic monarch.

Ordinary rebels in north focused on restoring Catholicism (religious banners, Mass at Durham).

(2) Student's own response.

Page 68

(1) **a**, **b**, **c** and **d**

Religion was very important for the ordinary rebels. The North was very Catholic, and resented the new Protestant Bishop of Durham. This was made clear by holding Mass in Durham cathedral. However, it was court politics and a loss of status that drove the leaders of the rebellion, making it more important than religion because without leadership the discontent of the ordinary people would not have led to rebellion*. The plot started with the aim of marrying Mary, Queen of Scots, to the Duke of Norfolk in order to secure the succession, as she had the best claim to the throne. It quickly developed into something much more important*: a plot to overthrow Elizabeth I. The earls greatly resented newcomers like Cecil and Leicester, who were Protestants like Elizabeth I. Overthrowing Elizabeth I's government and replacing her with the Catholic Mary would solve all the rebels' problems*: the Catholic earls would regain their political status and Catholicism would be restored. Religion was not the main reason for the rebellion, although it was important. Ultimately, however, the Revolt of the Northern Earls was about regime change stemming from court politics.

e Student's own response.

Page 69

(1) **Evidence yes:** the earls were Roman Catholic; the Duke of Norfolk was sympathetic to Catholicism; Mary, Queen of Scots, was Catholic; the rebels heard Mass in Durham cathedral; the courtiers that the earls resented were Protestant, e.g. Cecil, Leicester; the rebels were against the new Protestant Bishop of Durham, James Pilkington; northern England was far more Roman Catholic than Protestant.

(2) **Evidence no:** it started as a plot to secure the succession and its main aim was the marriage of Mary, Queen of Scots, to the Duke of Norfolk; the earls resented the rise of new courtiers, e.g. Cecil, Leicester; the rebellion started at court so court politics was more important; the plan developed to overthrow Elizabeth I with the help of Spanish soldiers in Hartlepool.

(3), **(4)** and **(5)** Student's own response.

Unit 8

Page 72

(1) **a** Conclusion 2

b Conclusion 3

(2) Amy's conclusion:

Overall, the most important reason why the Armada failed was Spain's poor planning and preparations. The English took advantage of communications problems **B**, **D** and poor Spanish cannonballs **C**, **E**, **F**. As English tactics used these weaknesses against Spain, this was also a very important reason the Armada was defeated, but it stems from Spain's preparations.

Sanjay's conclusion:

Spanish ships' design played the most important role in England's defeat of the Armada. They were no match against the English, who used their advantages well at Gravelines **A**, **E**. This shows that England's tactics were also important **C**, and disrupting Spain's communications by attacking Medina-Sidonia in the Channel **D** meant the Spanish were less well-prepared too.

(3) Student's own response, although Amy makes best use of supporting evidence in her conclusion – it is clearer to see which evidence she has used where.

Page 73

(1) **a** A, C, D

b B, C, D

c C

d A, B, C, D

(2) **a** Philip II made the decisions about tactics.

b Medina-Sidonia's fleet had been at sea for over ten weeks before it was first sighted in the Channel.

c Medina-Sidonia was unable to anchor his fleet off the Isle of Wight. *Or:* The English attacked the Armada off the Isle of Wight on 3–4 August 1588.

d English fireships scattered the Spanish fleet at Gravelines.

e The English had 24 galleons.

f The Duke of Parma's ships were too small to get ready in time.

Page 74

(3) **a** Philip II; because all the others were present at Gravelines.

b 15 August; because there was conflict between English and French ships on the other dates.

c false retreat; because the others were all tactics used by the English against the Armada.

④ **a** false
   b false
   c true
   d true
   e false

⑤ A = d; B = c; C = a; D = e; E = b

⑥ A week

⑦ Choose two from: more manoeuvrable; gun decks had enough space for cannon recoil; English galleons were faster (English cannon were mounted on smaller gun carriages, though this is not really ship design).

Page 75

① Although Spanish problems were quite significant in the failure of the Armada, because they gave England some advantages such as Parma not being ready for the Battle of Gravelines, England's ship design and tactics were more important. Ship design was most important because it gave England the advantages that enabled its tactics to be used. As English ships had better gun decks, they were able to fire faster than the Spanish at Gravelines. Combined with greater manoeuvrability, Spain's ships were no match for England's. England's naval leaders used these differences to inform their tactics, for example saving cannonballs for the final battle, as they knew this advantage would be most important. Spain's problems, such as poor communications, enabled England to make the most of the advantages but ultimately ship design was the foundation of the English victory.

② **a** B

   b A English tactics to attack Medina-Sidonia's ships made the most of the communications problems Spain had by not giving the Spanish time to prepare Parma's fleet.

   C Spain's poor resources helped but it was the English tactic of conserving cannonballs that enabled it to drive home the advantage when it mattered, at Gravelines

Page 76

① Leadership = F, G

   English tactics = A, C, D, H

   Spain's problems = A, B, D, E, F, H

②, ③ and ④ Student's own response

Page 77

①

Key characteristics of an effective conclusion		Which statement shows which characteristic?
a	Statement giving what you believe to be the most important factor	D, F
b	Statement on how far you agree with the stated factor	E
c	Explain your case for your choice of most important factor and why it is more important than any other factors	B
d	Bring in the relative importance of any other factors	C
e	Reinforce your conclusion about the most important factor and how it relates to the stated factor and other factors	A
f	Statement giving what you believe to be the most important factor	D, F

② D → B → A → E → C → F (although D → B → E → A → C → F can work too)

③ **a** Underline: A; D
   b Circle: B; C; D; E; F

Page 78

① Spain's problems

② English tactics enabled the English fleet to make the most of its advantages, such as superior ship design and Spain's problems. It was Spain's problems, however, that gave England some of its most important advantages. Communications not getting through led to Parma not being ready for Gravelines, which helped maximise England's tactical advantage in ship design. Also, Spain's poor supplies of cannonballs maximized England's advantage in firepower at Gravelines. England's naval leaders recognised the advantages Spain's problems gave them and they devised their tactics accordingly: English tactics relied upon Spain's problems.

③ England's naval leaders

④ Because it was Spain's problems that led to England's tactics; England's tactics depended upon Spain's problems.

⑤ and ⑥ Student's own response.

Page 79

① Student's own response.

Notes